Wildor Hollmann,
Dietrich Kurz,
Joachim Mester (Eds.)

Current Results on Health and Physical Activity

Series Club of Cologne Vol. 2

The Club of Cologne

Wildor Hollmann, Dietrich Kurz,
Joachim Mester (Eds.)

Current Results
on Health and
Physical Activity

Series Club of Cologne Vol. 2

HOFMANN-SCHATTAUER-VERLAG

Die Deutsche Bibliothek – Cataloging-in-Publication Data

Current results on health and physical activity /
The Club of Cologne. Wildor Hollmann ... (eds.).
– Schorndorf : Hofmann; Stuttgart ; New York : Schattauer, 2001
  (Series / Club of Cologne ; Vol. 2)
  ISBN 3-7780-6002-3

We are indebted to the following institute for their kind support

Otto Wolff von Amerongen-Stiftung

© 2001 by Verlag Karl Hofmann GmbH & Co.,
Steinwasenstraße 6–8, 73614 Schorndorf, Germany –
Internet http://www.hofmann-verlag.de

© 2001 by F. K. Schattauer Verlagsgesellschaft mbH,
Lenzhalde 3, 70192 Stuttgart, Germany –
Internet http://www.Schattauer.de

Layout: ART STUDIO GmbH, Köln

Printed in Germany
Printing and Binding: Druckerei und Verlag Karl Hofmann, Schorndorf.
Printed on acid-free paper.
ISBN 3-7780-6002-3 (Hofmann)
ISBN 3-7945-2164-1 (Schattauer)

Contents

The Club of Cologne

The Club of Cologne is an international society with voluntary membership representing the areas of science, sports, culture, politics and economics. The Club's organisational structure consists of presidency, board of directors, secretary general, and scientific council. Otto Wolf von Amerongen is the Club's president. All Club members firmly believe that there is untapped potential in sports that could be used to enrich human lives and to contribute to the solution of socio-cultural problems. The Club's goals are to uncover, support and develop this potential. However, with concern, club members also perceive trends and developments in sports that could interfere with its humane importance. Therefore, the Club's over-arching goal is to use scientific knowledge to further the conscientious development of sports. This includes analysis of international sports trends and development of future-oriented concepts.

The Club of Cologne supports scientific activities that can be expected to significantly contribute to the solution of important problems in the international development of sports or to advance the understanding of the role and meaning of sports in general. Typically, the Club does not fund specific research projects (as is the case with institutions such as BISp or DFG). Instead and following the motto "To Know What is Known," the Club of Cologne sponsors and facilitates the exchange of scientific knowledge in expert rounds and panel discussions, as well as through its support of publications and literature reviews.

Work at the Club of Cologne is currently organized in six fields of research; each led by one or more scientific experts:

➤ **Human Fitness and Health**
Prof. Dr. Dr. h.c. Wildor Hollmann,
Prof. Dr. Gert Peter Brüggemann
Both German Sport Uni. of Cologne

➤ **Culture and Social Systems**
Prof. Dr. Volker Rittner
German Sport University of Cologne

➤ **Ethics, Law and Politics**
Prof. Dr. Gunter Gebauer
Free University of Berlin

➤ **Ecology and Environment**
Dr. h.c. Johannes Eulering
Bottrop

➤ **Media and Communication**
Prof. Dr. Josef Hackforth,
Technical University of Munich

➤ **Work, Technology and Economics**
Prof. Dr. Klaus Heinemann
University of Hamburg

The Club's scientific council, led by chairman Prof. Dr. Dietrich Kurz, University of Bielefeld, in cooperation with the Club's secretary general Prof. Dr. Joachim Mester, German Sports University of Cologne, comprises the leaders of each of the six fields of research and coordinates the Club's scientific activities.

Further information on the Club of Cologne can be found at www.club-of-cologne.de. The site presents detailed information on the Club's bylaws, membership, activities, grant application criteria and guidelines; and it makes summary reports from the six different fields of research available.

Foreword

The members of the Club of Cologne are united in the conviction that sport exercised in the correct manner, can promote the individual's feeling of well-being. With this edition we want to support the dissemination of scientific knowledge which serves this aim. The discussed volume combines four work reports of international outstanding research groups of sports medicine. The importance of physical activity and sport for a healthy life is examined from four different angles.

The epidemiological studies of the research group of Ralph Paffenbarger (Stanford, USA) demonstrate at first from the bird's-eye view as it were, how much the probability of a long healthy life can be enhanced by regular physical activity apart from elements of lifestyle. Already in this study there can also be observed a statistical correlation between the life expectation of parents and their children. This suggests that genetic factors play a role as well. How strong is their impact?

This question has been dealt with by the team around Claude Bouchard (Baton Rouge, USA) for years. Their contribution offers a résumé of today's knowledge on this question incorporating the latest research results. These indicate that genetic factors not only influence the performance of the heart-circulation system (cardio-respiratory fitness) and the trainability (responsiveness to exercise), but also the tendency towards physical activity.

The relationship between physical activity and the immune system forms a young research area out of which important output on the health impact of sport can be expected in the near future. Bente Klarlund Pedersen (Copenhagen, Denmark), one of the world's leading research figure in this area, discusses the state-of-the-art of this issue. At first sight the report shows that physical activity can strengthen the immune system – but only if dosed correctly. Physical strain exceeding the usual load leads to a temporary weakening of the immune system. In this course it is also discussed under which circumstances physical activity decreases the cancer risk.

Following a suggestion of President Bush the decade of the brain was announced in 1989. Already a few years prior to this, in 1985, the research group around

Wildor Hollmann (Cologne, Germany) initiated experimental studies on the meaning of physical activity for the brain. Their work offers a comprehensive overview of how the extraordinary work of the brain can be described according to today's knowledge. Connections between motor control, mind and psyche are particularly emphasized. With this we begin to understand in which way each human develops his personality also through his movement habits.
All persons who are, like myself, convinced by experience of life that one's potential for a healthy and active life can be strengthened by sport, will find scientific corroboration but also significant restrictions in this volume. The knowledge presented here also underlines the political responsibility of all those who design the general conditions of our society under which people cultivate movement and sport as natural elements of their lives. From that point of view the volume is a good example for ideas and contributions of the Club of Cologne.

Prof. Dr. Otto Wolff von Amerongen
President Club of Cologne

Wildor Hollmann   Dietrich Kurz   Joachim Mester

Foreword

The empirical knowledge on the connection of physical activity, sport and health are not yet 50 years old, although physiological and sport medical researchers have worked on this topic for a far longer period. It is predominately the work of the American, Canadian and English epidemiologists which has produced a multitude of empirical findings which give a sounder basis for defining the interaction between physiological effects as well as providing social and health political explanations for a calculated and dosed continuous physical load. Apart from the connection of physical inactivity with morbidity, i.e. causing various organic diseases in the area of

the heart-circulation-system, scientific findings increasingly corroborate the biopositive effects on mortality. Statistics prove that individuals who deliberately subject themselves to regular and reasonably dosed physical exercise have a greater life expectancy.

Initiated by the undeniable empirical proof of the positive health benefits of physical activity and sport on the one hand and the nevertheless modest appreciation by the individual on the other hand, research institutions have developed, dedicating their particular attention to the phenomenon of lifestyle. It becomes clear that here lie exceptional scientific challenges. For this very reason, current epidemiological studies are devoting their energies to this phenomenon.

The rapid development of the research methods in the area of computer science and molecular-biological procedures has enabled the organ and functional systems to be placed at the centre of research attention, which could only be dealt with in a second rate manner over the last decades. Here one may name genetics, immunology and brain research in particular. Due to the large expenses of equipment, the number of epidemiological studies has been limited to date. Nevertheless this area also indicates the biological necessity of a chronic functional loading. The immuno-logical aspects and those of the brain metabolism, in particular, embody the scientific challenges of topical interest, by which the spectrum of the familiar biopositive connections between physical activity, sport and health can be broadened. Research into the area of genetic prerequisites supply the necessary basics for the understanding of such procedures, thus extending the limits of our knowledge.

Volume 2 of the Club of Cologne publications contains the current surveys of renowned international scientists in their field. In this way the Club of Cologne wishes to make a contribution in stimulating discussion on the connection between physical activity, sport and health on the basis of modern research results.

Prof. Dr. Dr. h.c. Wildor Hollmann
Prof. Dr. Dietrich Kurz
Prof. Dr. Dr. h.c. Joachim Mester
Series Editors Club of Cologne

Ralph S. Paffenbarger, Jr.[1,2] / I-Min Lee[2,3]

Age-Specific Physical Activities and Other Lifeway Patterns Influencing Health and Longevity

[1] *Stanford University School of Medicine Division of Epidemiology Department of Health Research and Policy Stanford, California*

[2] *Harvard School of Public Health Department of Epidemiology Boston, Massachusetts*

[3] *Harvard Medical School Brigham and Women's Hospital Division of Preventive Medicine Boston, Massachusetts*

Introduction

Only in the past 50 years or so have the unique and fundamental contributions of epidemiology been recognized as a means to understand the causes of chronic diseases, and as procedures to prevent and control such diseases. Both prospective and retrospective longitudinal observations have been used successfully to accomplish these purposes. The most reliable of such observations have examined host and environmental characteristics of cohorts of special populations in relation to the subsequent development of specific chronic diseases. For example, a random sample of the population in Framingham, Massachusetts, has been followed over a 50-year period, matching personal characteristics and habits-of-living collected from seriatim physical examinations with follow-up morbidity and mortality data (DAWBER, 1980, 257). In another example, large numbers of British physicians have been followed for more than 40 years with respect to cigarette smoking, as measured in postal questionnaires beginning in 1951 and again at various intervals thereafter, for its relation to cause-specific and all cause mortality (DOLL et al., 1994, 901–911). The same population has been followed in a 13-year period for the relation of alcohol consumption patterns to these same outcomes (DOLL et al., 1994, 911–918). As a final example, a myriad of populations have now been studied for physical activity and physiological fitness in relation to health, disease, and longevity, including the College Alumni Health Study (BLAIR et al., 1995, 135–136; US DEPARTMENT OF HEALTH AND HUMAN SERVICES, 1996, 278).

Findings

To evaluate the influence of various lifeway patterns, including physical activity, on risk of death from all causes, we present here some recent findings from survivors of a population of men who were born between 1896 and 1934, who entered Harvard College between

1916 and 1950, and who comprise part of the College Alumni Health Study (PAFFENBARGER et al., 1966, 314–328). Data from college time have been complemented with information on the midlife health status and health habits of these same men (alumni) as they relate to all cause mortality, and inversely, to survival up to recent time.

We have examined the experiences of 17,815 Harvard College alumni aged 45–84 years, who provided survey data through questionnaires on their personal characteristics, health status, and ways-of-living (lifeway patterns) in 1977. These patterns have then been related to all-cause mortality rates over a 16-year follow-up period from 1977 through 1992, yielding 254,636 man-years of observation when 4,399 alumni died. Relative and attributable risk estimates of mortality have been computed by selected levels of these lifeways adjusted for differences in age and potential confounding characteristics.

Demographics

Age-specific demographic data for this population are given in Table 1, which include the number of decedents and man-years of follow-up. The average age

of alumni in 1977 was 58.4 years, and of survivors in 1992, 72.6 years. To explore the influence of lifeway patterns on mortality at various stages of the aging process, we categorized the Harvard population into four 10-year age groups (45–54 through 75–84 years) and computed age- and multi-characteristic adjusted death rates for these groups. It is important to recognize that comparisons by lifeways were made among separate age groups, each followed for 16 years, and not as trackings of one 10-year age group as it passed through successive ages.

Table 2 gives frequency distributions of selected lifeway habits by stated age groups in 1977. With increasing age, lower proportions of men reported smoking cigarettes, especially heavy smoking; higher proportions were hypertensive, except for a leveling off in the oldest age groups; fewer were over-weight (a body mass index of 25–29) and obese (equal to or greater than 30); more reported a history of early parental mortality; and substantially more alumni self-reported physician-diagnosed chronic disease (coronary heart disease, stroke, diabetes mellitus, chronic obstructive pulmonary disease, or

Table 1: *Baseline and Follow-up Demographics of Harvard Alumni, from 1977 through 1992, by Age Groups in 1977*

Demographic Data	Age-Group (years) in 1977				
	45–54	55–64	65–74	75–84	TOTAL
No. of men in 1977	7,516	5,545	3,994	760	17,815
No. of deaths from 1977 through 1992	620	1,207	2,036	536	4,399
Man-years from 1977 through 1992	116,433	80,778	49,473	7,952	254,636
Average age (years ±SD*) in 1977	49.4 (3.2)	59.8 (2.9)	69.5 (2.8)	77.4 (1.8)	58.4 (9.3)
Average attained age (years ±SD*) in 1992	64.2 (3.7)	74.3 (4.1)	81.9 (5.0)	87.8 (5.0)	72.6 (8.5)

* Standard deviation

Age-Specific Physical Activities and Other Lifeway Patterns Influencing Health

Table 2: *Frequencies (Percent) of Selected Lifeway Patterns Among 17,815 Harvard Alumni, by Age Groups in 1977*

Age-Group (years) in 1977	Lifeway Pattern				
	45–54	55–64	65–74	75–84	Total
Cigarette habit	18.7	18.2	15.4	11.4	17.5
≥ 20 cigarettes per day	12.9	12.2	8.8	5.6	11.5
Hypertension	16.2	24.6	29.8	25.6	22.3
Body mass index (kg/m²)					
< 25	58.3	62.2	64.7	74.5	61.6
25–29	37.6	34.1	32.6	24.1	34.8
≥ 30	4.1	3.7	2.8	1.4	3.6
Alcohol intake (≥ 200 gm/week)	33.2	38.1	37.2	27.3	35.4
A parent dead before age 65 years	32.2	36.3	38.6	39.3	35.2
Chronic disease[1]	10.2	21.0	35.5	41.2	20.5
Walking (km/week)					
< 5	25.4	26.5	28.2	29.9	26.5
5–14	44.0	41.5	39.0	42.0	42.0
≥ 15	30.5	32.1	32.8	28.1	31.4
Stair climbing (floors/week)					
< 20	33.7	37.8	47.1	54.3	38.8
20–54	50.0	47.4	41.4	36.6	46.7
≥ 55	16.3	14.9	11.5	9.1	14.5
Sports play (most intense)					
None	8.7	12.4	21.9	32.2	13.7
Light (< 4.5 METs)	5.9	12.0	19.6	23.9	11.6
Moderate (4.5–5.9 METs)	6.0	7.0	9.4	9.5	7.2
Vigorous (≥ 6.0 METs)	79.5	68.6	49.1	34.4	67.5
Physical activity[2] (kcal/week)					
< 1000	27.7	32.4	41.7	53.9	33.4
1000–1999	29.5	28.3	26.2	24.9	28.2
≥ 2000	42.8	39.2	32.1	21.2	38.4

[1] Coronary heart disease, stroke, diabetes mellitus, chronic obstructive pulmonary disease, or cancer
[2] Walking, stair climbing, and sports play

cancer). No consistent trend by age was seen for alcohol consumption.

With respect to physical activity, the proportions of men who walked 15 or more km per week showed little trend from youngest to oldest age groups, while the proportions who climbed stairs equaling 55 or more floors per week and who played vigorous sports declined substantially with advancing age. In contrast, increased proportions of men were not involved in any sports play or played only light sports, that is, participated in activities requiring less than 4.5 metabolic equivalents (METs) of intensity. In fact, these trends represented a four-fold increase from youngest to oldest ages for both non-players and light sport players. And overall, alumni who expended less than 1000 kilocalories (kcal) per week in the summation of their activities showed a two-fold increase (28 percent for men aged 45–54 years and 54 percent for those aged 75–84).

It might be noted that age-trend patterns among smokers, overweights, stair climbers, and active (vigorous) men presumably had been influenced by previous (before 1977) mortality rates that were affected by these lifeway habits. For example, some men from the original population of Harvard College students who had experienced one or more detrimental influences may have died from such lifeways and not been available to report when the 1977 observations were made. Furthermore, interaction of all these lifeway patterns could have influenced morbidity and mortality rates in all age groups during the subsequent follow-up interval, and these remain unmeasured.

Lifeways and mortality

Table 3 presents rates and relative risks of all-cause mortality by selected levels of lifeway patterns over the follow-up period. Rates were adjusted for age differences, and relative risks were adjusted for age and each of the other patterns tabulated (multi-adjusted). Within lifeways, which generally distribute the population into thirds or customary and arbitrary levels, a relative risk of one was assigned to each lifeway with the highest mortality rate.

The more than 80 percent of men who were non-smokers of cigarettes were at essentially one-half the risk of death among heavy smokers, and light smokers about two-thirds of that risk. Normotensive men experienced only three-quarters the risk of hypertensives.

Body mass index and alcohol consumption patterns indicated U-shaped distributions of mortality when the populations were examined in approximately thirds, with mid-range levels showing the lowest death rates, suggesting that both lower and higher levels of each characteristic carried a higher risk. Early parental mortality (one or both parents dead before age 65 years) was associated with about a 15 percent increased alumnus mortality in the follow-up interval. And the presence of a potentially lethal chronic disease, which characterized 18 percent of the man-years of experience, was a strong predictor of increased alumni mortality during follow-up.

With respect to physical activity, results in Table 3 echo findings from questionnaires returned by Harvard alumni in 1962 or 1966 with follow-up through 1978 (PAFFENBARGER et al., 1978, 161–175). The consistent pattern here reaffirms the inverse relation between both the quantity and the intensity of physical activity with the risk of all-cause mortality. All major trends related to physical activity level (i. e. the association between lower death rate and higher levels of walking, stair climbing, sports play, and combinations of these activities measured in kcal per week) were strongly significant. Gradients of benefit from more active lifeways were consistent throughout, including those activities that required even low levels of metabolic intensity (PAFFENBARGER et al., 1986, 605–613).

Table 4 gives age-specific, multi-characteristic adjusted relative risks of death, by the same lifeway patterns given in Table 3. In most instances, these gradients of association for the separate age groups ran parallel to those for age- and

Table 3: Adjusted Rates[1] and Relative Risks of Death[2] Among Harvard Alumni[3], from 1977 through 1992, by Lifeway Patterns in 1977

Lifeway Pattern	Man-Years %	No. of Deaths	Deaths/ 10,000 M-Y	RR of Death (95% CI)	P of Trend
Cigarette habit (no./day)					
≥ 20	11.0	689	309.0	1.00	< 0.001
< 20	5.8	301	208.0	0.69 (0.60–0.79)	
none	83.2	3,380	155.9	0.53 (0.49–0.57)	
Blood pressure status					
Hypertension	21.0	1,388	225.1	1.00	< 0.001[4]
Normotension	79.0	3,003	155.9	0.75 (0.70–0.80)	
Body mass index (kg/m²)					
≥ 26	23.5	1,003	190.9	1.00	0.312
24–25	31.5	1,211	159.7	0.87 (0.80–0.95)	
< 24	45.0	2,059	174.3	0.94 (0.87–1.02)	
Alcohol intake (gm/week)					
≥ 200	35.1	1,671	186.4	1.00	0.131
50–199	36.8	1,380	157.7	0.92 (0.86–0.99)	
< 50	28.1	1,326	172.3	0.95 (0.88–1.02)	
A parent dead before age 65 years					
Both	4.3	254	209.2	1.00	0.010
One	30.4	1,422	179.8	0.87 (0.76–1.00)	
Neither	65.4	2,607	165.0	0.84 (0.74–0.95)	
Chronic disease[5]					
Present	17.6	1,747	284.1	1.00	< 0.001[4]
Absent	82.4	2,639	137.0	0.51 (0.48–0.55)	
Walking (km/week)					
< 5	25.8	1,284	200.7	1.00	< 0.001
5–14	42.3	1,698	167.1	0.90 (0.83–0.96)	
≥ 15	31.9	1,249	152.8	0.87 (0.80–0.94)	
Stair climbing (floors/week)					
< 20	37.5	2,025	194.0	1.00	< 0.001
20–54	47.5	1,764	157.0	0.89 (0.83–0.95)	
≥ 55	14.9	506	147.2	0.86 (0.78–0.95)	
Sports play (weekly)					
None	27.2	1,903	218.8	1.00	< 0.001
Light only (< 4.5 METs)	10.5	628	178.8	0.84 (0.76–0.92)	
Moderately-vigorous (≥ 4.5 METs)	62.3	1,777	140.1	0.73 (0.69–0.79)	
Physical activity[6] (kcal/week)					
< 1000	31.5	1,908	213.5	1.00	< 0.001
1000–1999	28.7	1,101	158.4	0.81 (0.75–0.87)	
≥ 2000	39.8	1,299	144.3	0.75 (0.70–0.81)	

[1] Age-adjusted
[2] Adjusted for age and each of the other lifeway patterns listed; 95 percent confidence interval
[3] 17,815 men; 4,399 deaths; 254,636 man-years
[4] P value
[5] Coronary heart disease, stroke, diabetes mellitus, chronic obstructive pulmonary disease, or cancer
[6] Walking, stair climbing, and sports play

Table 4: *Age-Specific Relative Risks of Death[1] Among Harvard Alumni[2], from 1977 through 1992, by Lifeway Patterns in 1977*

Lifeway Pattern	Age-Group (years) in 1977 [P of Trend]			
	45–54	55–64	65–74	75–84
Cigarette habit (no./day)				
≥ 20	1.00 [< 0.001]	1.00 [< 0.001]	1.00 [< 0.001]	1.00 [0.275]
< 20	0.59	0.61	0.88	0.75
none	0.41	0.46	0.66	0.78
Blood pressure status				
Hypertension	1.00 [0.001³]	1.00 [< 0.001³]	1.00 [0.001³]	1.00 [0.001³]
Normotension	0.72	0.66	0.85	0.73
Body mass index (kg/m²)				
≥ 26	1.00 [0.002]	1.00 [0.179]	1.00 [0.229]	1.00 [0.608]
24–25	0.66	0.91	0.93	1.02
< 24	0.74	0.90	1.05	1.06
Alcohol intake (gm/week)				
≥ 200	1.00 [0.845]	1.00 [0.882]	1.00 [0.048]	1.00 [0.343]
50–199	0.98	0.81	0.97	0.98
< 50	1.02	1.04	0.89	0.90
A parent dead before age 65 years				
Both	1.00 [0.389]	1.00 [0.042]	1.00 [0.051]	1.00 [0.325]
One	0.93	0.85	0.91	0.82
Neither	0.87	0.79	0.85	0.97
Chronic disease[5]				
Present	1.00 [< 0.001³]	1.00 [< 0.001³]	1.00 [< 0.001³]	1.00 [<0.001³]
Absent	0.36	0.44	0.58	0.69
Walking (km/week)				
< 5	1.00 [0.653]	1.00 [0.005]	1.00 [0.055]	1.00 [0.002]
5–14	0.85	0.87	0.95	0.75
≥ 15	0.95	0.80	0.89	0.69
Stair climbing (floors/week)				
< 20	1.00 [0.410]	1.00 [0.322]	1.00 [< 0.001]	1.00 [0.692]
20–54	0.97	0.88	0.87	0.94
≥ 55	1.14	0.97	0.69	0.98
Sports play (weekly)				
None	1.00 [< 0.001]	1.00 [< 0.001]	1.00 [< 0.001]	1.00 [0.008]
Light only (< 4.5 METs)	0.79	0.91	0.81	0.78
Moderately-vigorous (≥ 4.5 METs)	0.69	0.71	0.77	0.76
Physical activity[5] (kcal/week)				
< 1000	1.00 [0.228]	1.00 [< 0.001]	1.00 [< 0.001]	1.00 [0.001]
1000–1999	0.87	0.78	0.85	0.70
≥ 2000	0.89	0.76	0.73	0.73

[1] Computed from death rates adjusted for age and each of the other lifeway patterns listed
[2] 17,815 men; 4,399 deaths; 254,636 man-years
[3] P value
[4] Coronary heart disease, stroke, diabetes mellitus, chronic obstructive pulmonary disease, or cancer
[5] Walking, stair climbing, and sports play

multi-characteristic adjusted relative risks. However, there are some exceptions to these similarities that may offer useful implications for preventive intervention at given ages. For example, an inverse relation with death for body mass index was evident only for the youngest men. Other age groups failed to show this relation of higher death risk for overweight and obese men. At the oldest end of the age range, cigarette smoking was not significantly related to death from all causes, again perhaps because smoking had taken a considerable toll in prior years, leaving a substantially reduced population of smokers at risk before they turned 75 years.

With respect to measures of energy expenditure, both walking and stair climbing in the youngest men (45–54 years) were unrelated to mortality, and even the total of activities measured in kilocalories per week were not significantly related to death from all causes. Only sports play was related (inversely and significantly) to death in the 16-year follow-up period for those youngest men. Moderately-vigorous and vigorous sports play (4.5 METs or more of intensity) clearly was the strongest predictor of reduced mortality in each of the age groups studied.

Changes in lifeways and mortality

We have tested the hypothesis that favorable changes in lifeway habits would reduce risk of early mortality. Earlier observations in this same population had shown that former university athletes retained lower cardiovascular disease risk and experienced delayed mortality only if they maintained an active way-of-life in middle age (PAFFEN-BARGER et al., 1978, 161–175). Also, these same college students who converted from sedentary habits to a physically active lifeway as alumni reduced their risks of disease and death to the same low level of former university athletes who were still active. To examine any further effect of change or lack of change of lifeway habits on mortality, we computed death rates, 1977 through 1992, for that group of alumni who had reported on their lifeways in 1962 or 1966 and again in 1977 (PAFFENBARGER et al., 1993, 538–545). These analyses comprised 14,787 men of whom 3,528 died during 212,410 man-years of observation.

We compared the experiences of alumni who had smoked cigarettes in the 1960's with those who had dropped the habit by 1977, together with those who had never smoked. The risk of untimely death in the latter two categories were 27 and 47 percent lower, respectively. Over this same interval of observation, from the 1960's to 1977, as compared with normotensives, men who became hypertensive experienced a 23 percent higher risk of mortality; long-term hypertensives, a 41 percent higher risk. Alumni who had increased their body mass index by two units or more experienced a 27 percent higher risk of death than men who maintained their index within one-half a unit; men who lost weight and decreased their body mass index by two units or more experienced a 44 percent higher risk of death in the 16-year follow-up.

Alumni who had increased or decreased their energy expenditure by less than 250 kcal per week between the 1960's and 1977 were placed in an "unchanged" category and considered to have a relative risk of 1.0 (Figure 1, upper panel). Compared with this referent standard,

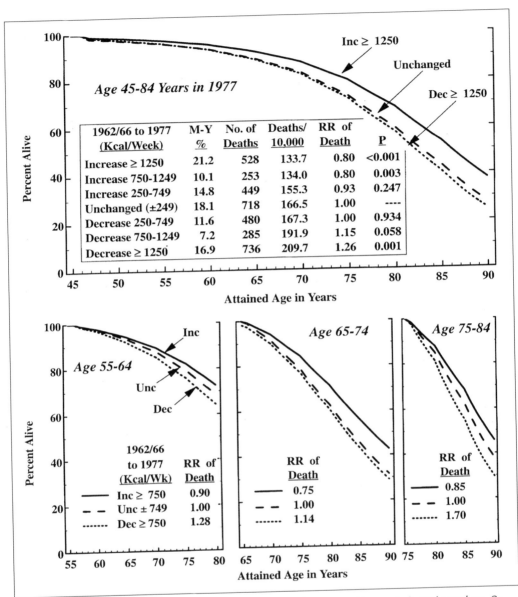

Figure 1: Survivorship curves and relative risks of death, among Harvard alumni aged 45–84 years, between 1977 and 1992, according to change or lack of change in physical activity (kcal per week) between 1962 or 1966 and 1977. Curves and relative risks were adjusted for age, cigarette smoking habit, blood pressure status, body mass index, alcohol consumption, early parental mortality and chronic disease. "Unchanged" categories represents men in upper panel who had increased or decreased their energy expenditure by less than 250 kcal per week; bottom panel, by less than 750 kcal per week (see text). Findings are derived from epidemiological follow-up of 14,787 men during which 3,528 men died in 212,410 man-years of observation.

gradient reductions in mortality were observed with increased levels of physical activity, and gradient increases in mortality with decreased levels of energy output. At the extremes of this gradient, men who had increased their energy expenditure by 1,250 kcal per week or more had a 20 percent lower risk of death than men in the unchanged category; men who decreased their activity by that much, a 26 percent higher risk. Also (not shown), men who had taken up moderately vigorous sports play experienced a 22 percent lower mortality rate than men who had not played sports; men who had dropped sports play, experienced a 16 percent higher mortality rate. These same patterns of mortality were experienced by each of the four 10-year age groups; that is, with increased physical activity, a decreased mortality experience, and vice versa. Patterns for the three eldest age groups are given in Figure 1 (lower panel) where the "unchanged" categories were defined as alumni who had increased or decreased their energy expenditure by less than 750 kcal per week.

Estimates of mortality avoidance

Population attributable risks express the percentage reductions in death that might have been achieved in the total group of 17,815 alumni if all the men with specified adverse conditions had converted them to healthful levels, and if all alumni who already followed favorable lifeways had maintained them during the follow-up period. Attributable risks assume that associations represent cause-and-effect relations, and that unmeasured influencing variables are equally distributed among groups being compared. Table 5 gives age-specific and total attributable risks together with 95 percent confidence intervals for the latter. Accordingly, in this population the number of deaths during follow-up might have been reduced by 34 percent if every man had abstained from cigarette smoking. Absence of hypertension in the population might have led to 18 percent fewer deaths; a body mass index of less than 26 units, to nearly 7 percent fewer deaths; and lack of specified (life-threatening) chronic disease, to more than 36 percent fewer deaths. Alcohol consumption of less than 200 gm per week and lack of parental mortality before age 65 years would have had lesser effects. The number of deaths during the 16-year follow-up might have been reduced by 14 percent if every man had expended a minimum of 1000 kcal per week in walking, stair climbing, and recreational (sports play) activities. As performed, walking less than 15 km per week would have had a minimal effect (about two percent fewer deaths), but stairclimbing 20 or more floors per week, and all intensities of sports play, would have led to appreciably lower numbers of fatalities (nearly five to more than 15 percent fewer).

Estimates of delayed mortality (Table 5) indicated some sizeable differences among specific age groups. For example, cigarette smoking and the presence of a chronic disease proved especially harmful for alumni aged 45–64 years, as did overweight-for-height for men 45–54 years in 1977. A sedentary lifestyle (expending less than 1000 kcal per week) for men aged 55 years and over, and failure to play sports, especially moderately-vigorous sports, by younger men, apparently took a heavy toll. If all men had included sports play in their weekly

Table 5: Attributable Risks of Death (Percent)[1] Among Harvard Alumni[2], from 1977 through 1992, from Adverse Lifeway Patterns, by Age Groups in 1977

Age-Group (years) in 1977	Adverse Lifeway Pattern				
	45–54	55–64	65–74	75–84	TOTAL (95% CI)
Cigarette habit	43.0	41.1	26.2	12.8	34.0 (30.2–37.6)
Hypertension	22.6	25.3	10.6	20.7	18.3 (14.6–21.9)
Body mass index (kg/m²) ≥ 26	21.9	7.5	−0.4	−4.1	6.8 (1.5–11.8)
Alcohol intake ≥ 200 gm/week	0.5	5.9	3.9	4.2	4.2 (0.5–7.9)
A parent dead before age 65	4.4	6.2	4.9	−8.6	3.9 (0.2–7.4)
Chronic disease[3]	57.2	44.6	29.1	19.7	36.5 (34.0–37.6)
Walking < 15 km/week	−1.4	4.2	3.0	5.3	2.4 (0.5–4.4)
Stair climbing < 20 floors/week	0.8	7.1	9.2	3.8	7.2 (4.1–10.1)
No sports play	22.8	18.1	11.9	9.8	15.3 (12.3–18.2)
No light sports play (< 4.5 METs)	6.1	3.2	4.9	5.4	4.5 (2.3–6.6)
No moderately-vigorous sports play (≥ 4.5 METs)	18.0	15.5	6.8	5.0	11.4 (9.0–13.7)
Physical activity[4] < 1000 kcal/week	9.5	17.2	12.6	13.8	14.1 (11.1–16.9)

[1] Adjusted for age and each of the other lifeway patterns listed; 95 percent confidence interval
[2] 17,815 men; 4,399 deaths; 254,636 man-years
[3] Coronary heart disease, stroke, diabetes mellitus, chronic obstructive pulmonary disease, or cancer
[4] Walking, stair climbing, and sports play

agenda, deaths might have been reduced by 23 percent among those of youngest age, by 12 to 18 percent among men of midrange ages, and even 10 percent among the oldest age groups during the 16-year follow-up.

Added years of life
The mortality and survival experiences of the Harvard alumni during the 16-year follow-up period were used to develop estimates of years of added life gained (up to age 90 years) from favorable as opposed to detrimental lifeway patterns (Table 6). Estimates were made for ten year age groups and for the total age span as of 1977. Younger men obviously benefited more than their elders from following a favorable pattern. Additional life for not smoking versus smoking cigarettes was nearly three years, and one and one-half years for remaining normotensive as opposed to becoming hypertensive. Men who maintained a body mass index of less than 26 units might have gained one-half a year as compared with men who weighed more for their height. Men who consumed less than 200 gm of alcohol per week and had long-lived parents might have added one-third extra year over the life expectancy for men with corresponding detrimental lifeway patterns. Men who had avoided chronic disease as of the 1977 questionnaire assessment might have gained an extra four years over men with

Table 6: Added Years of Life Gained[1] (to age 90) from Favorable Lifeway Patterns Among Harvard Alumni[2], as Estimated from Death Rates[3] from 1977 through 1992

Age-Group (years) in 1977	Favorable Lifeway Pattern				
	45–54	55–64	65–74	75–84	Total (95% CI)
No cigarette smoking	3.33	2.96	2.31	1.48	2.91 (2.47–3.34)
Normotension	1.79	1.58	1.23	0.78	1.55 (1.19–1.92)
Body mass index (kg/m²) < 26	0.55	0.50	0.39	0.25	0.49 (0.10–0.87)
Alcohol intake < 200 gm/week	0.42	0.37	0.29	0.19	0.37 (0.03–0.70)
Both parents alive ≥ 65 years	0.39	0.35	0.27	0.17	0.34 (0.01–0.67)
No chronic disease	4.58	3.96	2.99	1.86	3.91 (3.53–4.30)
Walking ≥ 15 km/week	0.48	0.43	0.34	0.22	0.42 (0.08–0.77)
Stair climbing ≥ 20 floors/week	0.82	0.73	0.58	0.37	0.72 (0.40–1.04)
Any sports play	1.73	1.54	1.20	0.75	1.51 (1.17–1.86)
Moderately-vigorous sports play (≥ 4.5 METs)	1.65	1.47	1.14	0.71	1.44 (1.10–1.78)
Physical activity[4] ≥ 1000 kcal/week	1.59	1.42	1.10	0.69	1.39 (1.06–1.73)

[1] LIfe-table estimates based on favorable versus detrimental lifeway patterns and death rates adjusted for age and each of the other patterns listed; 95 percent confidence interval
[2] 17,815 men; 4,399 deaths; 254,636 man-years
[3] No coronary heart disease, stroke, diabetes, chronic obstructive pulmonary disease, or cancer
[4] Walking, stair climbing, and sports play

life-threatening conditions.
Walking 15 or more km, stair climbing 20 or more floors, playing sports, and playing moderately-vigorous sports each week versus their opposites were estimated to yield nearly one-half, 0.72, one and one-half, and 1.44 added years of life, respectively. Totaling these activities showed the estimated survival gain by alumni expending 1000 kcal per week or more as compared with less active men to exceed an extra year. Men of all ages, even the oldest (all of whom were followed until death or age 90 years) experienced at least an extra one-half year by being active as compared with being sedentary. Of further importance was the observation that these physically active alumni, as contrasted with

their less active counterparts, reported that they "felt younger than their years", and were more likely to be "feeling fine and enjoying life" (PAFFENBARGER et al., 1993, 538–545).
These actuarial estimates indicate only what might have been if these favorable lifeway patterns had existed for the whole population during the follow-up period. But they also afford opportunity to predict the logical extension or outcome for sometime in the future.

Discussion
The findings reported here on college alumni suggest a protective effect against untimely death from abstention of cigarette smoking; maintenance of normotension and a lean body mass;

avoidance of chronic disease; and participation in physical activities, especially moderately-vigorous or vigorous sports play. These findings pertain in all age groups studied, and therefore an indication of additional years of life expectancy. To the extent that these alumni reduced their smoking, received treatment for hypertension, and increased their physical exercise habits since 1977, when these lifeway patterns were assessed, such changes in lifeways would minimize the importance of the healthful patterns reported here. Thus, the true strength of the protective effect of these lifeway patterns would be even *larger* than observed. Nevertheless, the estimates of added years of life gained reflect the self-reported experience of college men, already recognized as long-lived, whose level of affluence and social behavior might differ from other populations, and this might invite caution against unwarranted generalizations to certain other populations.

Nonetheless, the opportunity to examine long-range parallels between findings based on experience of student days and these same alumni many years later give a different dimension to the study of lifeways that influence health. For example, if it is postulated that university sports play reflects, at least in part, a selective attribute of personal health (e.g. cardiovascular fitness), recent findings show that such selection alone is insufficient to explain delayed death in later adult (alumni) years. Alumni who had not been especially athletic as students, but rated high physical activity status at middle and advanced age, were at lower risk of mortality than former athletes whose later exercise level did not include moderately vigorous sports play.

The medical treatment of such chronic diseases as cardiovascular ailments and diabetes mellitus, and the management of such intermediate variables as abnormal blood lipoprotein profiles and impaired glucose tolerance, may defer mortality and extend longevity. Yet, the effect of adequate physical activity is partly independent of these influences and it counteracts many detrimental variables through metabolic and other processes. Even when other means of health promotion and disease prevention are used to increase longevity, the relevance of adequate physical activity is likely to remain.

References

BLAIR, S. N.; BOUCHARD, C.; GYARFAS, I.; HOLLMANN, W.; IWANE, H.; KNUTTGEN, H. G.; LÜSCHEN, G.; MESTER, J.; MORRIS, J. N.; PAFFENBARGER, R. S., JR.; RENSTRÖM, P.; SONNENSCHEIN, W.; VUORI, I. (WHO/FIMS Committee on Physical Activity for Health) (1995): Exercise for health. In: *Bulletin of the World Health Organization, 73,* 135–136.

DAWBER, T. R. (1980): The Framingham Study: *The Epidemiology of Atherosclerotic Disease.* Harvard: Harvard University Press.

DOLL, R.; PETO, R.; HALL, E.; WHEATLEY, K.; GRAY, R. (1994): Mortality in relation to consumption of alcohol: 13 years' observations on male British doctors. In: *British Medical Journal, 309,* 911–918.

DOLL, R.; PETO, R.; WHEATLEY, K.; GRAY, R.; SUTHERLAND, I. (1994): Mortality in relation to smoking: 40 years' observations on male British doctors. In: *British Medical Journal, 309,* 901–911.

PAFFENBARGER, R. S., JR.; HYDE, R. T.; WING, A. L.; HSIEH, C. -C. (1986): Physical activity, all-cause mortality, and longevity of college alumni. In: *New England Journal of Medicine, 314,* 605–613.

PAFFENBARGER, R. S., JR.; HYDE, R. T.; WING, A. L.; LEE, I. -M.; JUNG, D. L.; KAMPERT, J. B. (1993): The association of changes in physical-activity level and other lifestyle characteristics with mortality among men. In: *New England Journal of Medicine, 328,* 538–545.

PAFFENBARGER, R. S., JR.; WING, A. L.; HYDE, R. T. (1978): Physical activity as an index of heart attack risk in college alumni. In: *American Journal of Epidemiology, 108,* 161–175.

PAFFENBARGER, R. S., JR.; WOLF, P. A.; NOTKIN, J.; THORNE, M. C. (1966): Chronic disease in former college students: I. Early precursors of fatal coronary heart disease. In: *American Journal of Epidemiology, 83,* 314–328.

US DEPARTMENT OF HEALTH AND HUMAN SERVICES (1996): P*hysical Activity and Health: A Report of the Surgeon General.* United States Department of Health and Human Services. Centers for Disease Control and Prevention, National Center for Chronic Disease Prevention and Health Promotion.

Tuomo Rankinen / Louis Pérusse / Claude Bouchard

Genetic Aspects of Physical Activity, Cardiorespiratory Fitness and the Response to Regular Exercise

Physical Activity Sciences Laboratory, Division of Kinesiology, Department of Social and Preventive Medicine, Faculty of Medicine, Laval University, Québec, Canada

Abstract

The studies summarized in this review suggest that level of physical activity and energy expenditure related to physical activity as well as sports participation are characterized by significant familial resemblance. Children whose parents are active are more likely to be active than children of sedentary parents. Results from twin and family studies suggest that genetic factors could contribute to this famial resemblance and heritabilities ranging from about 20% to 50% have been reported. However, these estimates should be considered as maximal heritabilities as they probably reflect the contribution of both genetic and cultural inheritance. No attempts have been made so far in humans to identify DNA sequence variation or genes that could be involved in determining activity level or energy expenditure related to physical activity. However, a few promising candidate genes have been identified from animal studies. These include the dopamine transporter and dopamine receptor D2 genes and a gene indentified in the fruit fly affecting its food-search behaviour.

The genetic determinants of cardiorespiratory fitness and related sub-pheno-types have been more extensively studied than physical activity level. The evidence accumulated so far suggests heritabilities in the range of 25% to 50% for maximal oxygen consumption and submaximal exercise capacity, the highest heritabilities generally derived from twins studies. There is also good evidence that some of the determinants of these performance phenotypes, such as cardiac dimensions, skeletal muscle fiber type and metabolic properties and exercise blood pressure are influenced by genetic factors with heritabilities in the range of 40% to 75%. There is now solid evidence to the effect that the response of cardiorespiratory fitness and related sub-phenotypes to exercise training is partly modulated by genetic factors. Evidence obtained primarily from studies performed with identical twins have shown a consistently higher within- than between-pair resemblance in the response of several health-related fitness phenotypes to regular exercise. The search for the genes involved in cardiorespiratory fitness and in its response to training is still in its infancy. Human molecular studies reported so far have shown that genetic variation in a few candidate genes encoded in the nuclear or in the mitochondrial genome could be involved. Although some studies suggest that genes like the muscle creatine kinase (CKMM), the angiotensin-converting enzyme (ACE) or the erythropoietin receptor (EPOR) could be involved, it is too early to draw any definitive conclusion about their implications. A variety of research designs and technologies are currently being used to identify the relevant genes and mutations. The genetic dissection of physical activity level and fitness phenotypes as well as of the trainability of fitness indicators is a very complex undertaking but one likely to be achieved early in this millenium.

1. Introduction

Over a period of several decades, a large number of genetic studies have been conducted in order to quantify the respective contributions of genetic and non-genetic factors to the population variance in the occurrence of complex multifactorial diseases, as well as in risk factors for these diseases. The successful genetic dissection of these complex disease phenotypes requires that lifestyle and environmental factors are also taken into account. Physical activity represents an important component of a healthy lifestyle. There is now good evidence that regular physical activity could play a protective role against several common diseases such as coronary heart disease, diabetes, stroke, obesity and cancer. Physical activity and physical fitness, particularly cardiorespiratory fitness, are important determinants of health-related fitness. The existence of genetic effects in these

health-related fitness phenotypes as well as in their reponses to regular exercise has considerable public health implications. It implies that not everybody is equally prone to engage in physical activity, that the potential of physical activity to reduce the risk level for several common chronic diseases is not the same for all individuals and that preventive medicine and public health strategies could be developed for population subgroups with an emphasis on the high-risk individuals.

The purpose of this chapter is to provide an overview of the role of genetic factors in physical activity level, cardiorespiratory fitness and to illustrate the role of some candidate genes in modulating the responsiveness of health-related fitness phenotypes to regular exercise.

2. Genetics of physical activity level

Energy expenditure is a complex phenotype comprised of several components: basal and resting metabolic rates, thermic effect of food, and energy expenditure of activity including the energy cost of specific activities. Evidence indicates that genetic factors contribute to interindividual differences in levels of habitual physical activity but few studies have thus far addressed this issue.

2.1 Evidence from genetic epidemiology studies

Studies on the genetics of physical activity level or the amount of energy expended for daily physical activity are not extensive. Evidence from both twin and family studies suggest that genetic factors could be involved in the determination of physical activity level. Several

Table 1: *Summary of the intraclass correlations from twin studies for physical activity level and physical activity -related phenotypes*

Source	Phenotype	Age	Sex	Number of pairs		Correlation coefficients	
				MZ	DZ	MZ	DZ
Kaprio et al., 1981	Total physical activity	> 18	Male	1537	3507	0.57	0.26
Koopmans et al., 1994	Sports participation	18–22	Male	249	241	0.89	0.60
			Female	329	303	0.85	0.72
Aarnio et al., 1997	Leisure-time physical activity outside the school	16	Male	147	191	0.72	0.45
			Female	231	179	0.64	0.41
Lauderdale et al., 1997	Intermittent moderate activities	33–51	Male	1006	530	0.38	0.53
	Jogging / running (> 10 miles/wk)					0.52	0.58
	Strenuous racquet sports (>5 h/wk)					0.39	0.12
	Bicycling (> 50 miles/wk)					0.07	0.28
	Swimming (> 2 miles/wk)					0.14	0.35
McGue et al., 1993	Self-rated ability on athletic competition	27–80	Male	226	202	0.50[a]	0.26[a]
		27–86	Female	452	345		
McGuire et al., 1994	Perceived athletic self-competence	10–18	Male	45	49	0.58[a]	0.23[a]
		10–18	Female	47	48		

[a] = coefficients adjusted for sex

twin studies have addressed the role of genetic factors in physical activity level and the findings from these studies are summarized in Table 1.

In 1,537 monozygous (MZ) and 3,057 dizygous (DZ) male twin pairs over 18 years of age from the Finnish Twin Registry (KAPRIO et al., 1981), information on intensity and duration of activity, years of participation in a given activity, physical activity on the job, and subjective opinion of the subject's own activity level was obtained from a questionnaire. These variables were submitted to factor analysis to generate a factor score of physical activity that was used to compute correlations within MZ and DZ twin pairs. The results indicated an estimated heritability of 62% for age-adjusted physical activity level. HELLER et al., reported a significantly higher concor-

dance within 94 pairs of MZ twins than within 106 pairs of DZ twins for participation in vigorous exercise in the past two weeks, and estimated the heritability of this phenotype at about 39% (HELLER et al., 1988). In another cohort of Finnish twins aged 16 years, leisure-time physical activity level outside the school was assessed using a questionnaire with two questions: one concerning the frequency and the other the intensity of the activities (AARNIO et al., 1997). Based on these two questions the subjects were assigned to one of five classes of activity level. The results revealed greater intraclass correlations for MZ twins that for DZ twins for activity level. In MZ twins, the correlations were 0.64 (n = 231) for girls and 0.72 (n = 147) for boys whereas the correlations in DZ twins were 0.41 and 0.45 for girls (n = 179) and boys (n = 191), respectively. In the USA Vietnam Era Twin Registery (VETR) cohort, levels of moderate and vigorous activities were assessed using a mixed-mode mail and telephone survey (LAUDERDALE et al., 1997). The cohort consisted of 3344 male twin pairs aged 33 to 51 years. A clear pattern of familial clustering of both moderate and vigorous activities were observed, with the odds ratios for a twin to engage in physical activity when his co-twin also engaged in the same activity ranging from 1.25 (95%CI 1.21–1.30) to 4.60 (2.89–7.30). For the heritability analyses, only those twin pairs who saw each other at least once per month as adults were selected. Twin correlations for all activities were greater in MZ pairs (n = 1006) than in DZ pairs (n = 530). However, the heritability estimates were greater for vigorous activities such as jogging/running (0.53), racquet sports (0.48) and bicycling (0.58) than for moderate activities (from 0.12 to 0.40).

Participation in sports activity may be influenced by genetic factors. In a study based on 1,294 families including both parents and 1,587 pairs of MZ and DZ twins, an estimated heritability of 45% for sports participation was reported (KOOPMANS et al., 1994). The remaining phenotypic variance was attributed to shared familial environment (44%) and environmental factors unique to each individual (11%). Moreover, psychological factors affecting sports participation may be characterized by a significant genetic component. In a cohort of 678 MZ and 547 DZ twin pairs, aged 27 - 86 years, an index of self-rated ability in athletic competition showed a genetic effect of 50.5% while the remaining 49.5% of the variance was due to nons-

hared environmental factors (McGUE et al., 1993). A very similar estimate of genetic effect was derived from data of 92 MZ twin pairs, 97 DZ twin pairs and 94 full sibling pairs, aged 10 to 18 years. The genetic effect for perceived athletic self-competence was 54% whereas non-shared environmental factors contributed an additional 42% of the variance (McGUIRE et al., 1994).

Physical activity levels and patterns in children and their parents tend to be similar, but studies of familial aggregation of activity level and sports participation are relatively few. In 100 children, aged 4 to 7 years, and 99 mothers and 92 fathers from the Framingham Children's Study (MOORE et al., 1991), data on habitual physical activity were obtained with an accelerometer for about 10 hours per day for an average of 9 days in children and 8 days in fathers and mothers over the course of one year. Active fathers (accelerometer counts per hour above the median) or active mothers were more likely to have active offspring than inactive fathers or mothers, with odds ratios of 3.5 and 2.0, respectively. When both parents were active, the children were 5.8 times more likely to be active as children of two inactive parents. These results are thus compatible with the notion that genetic or other factors transmitted across generations predispose a child to be active or inactive.

Familial resemblance in leisure-time energy expenditure was estimated in data from the 1981 Canada Fitness Survey (PÉRUSSE et al., 1988). A total of 18,073 individuals living in households across Canada completed a questionnaire on physical activity habits. Detailed information on the frequency, duration and intensity of activities performed on a daily, weekly, monthly and yearly basis was used to estimate average daily energy expenditure (per kg of body weight) for each individual. Familial correlations were 0.28, 0.12 and 0.21 for spouses (n = 1,024 pairs), parents and offspring (n = 1,622 pairs), and sibling pairs (n = 1,036), respectively. The lower correlations in parent-offspring and sibling pairs compared to spouses suggest only a small contribution of genetic factors in the familial aggregation of leisure-time energy expenditure.

In the Quebec Family Study (QFS), path analysis procedures (PÉRUSSE et al., 1989) were used to estimate the relative contribution of genetic and non-genetic factors to activity level. Two different indicators of physical activity, habitual physical activity and participation in moderate to vigorous physical activity, were obtained from a 3-day activity record completed by 1,610 members from 375 families encompassing nine types of relatives by descent or adoption. Most of the variation in the two indicators of habitual physical activity level was accounted for by non-transmissible environmental factors, with values reaching 71% for habitual physical activity and 88% for exercise participation. The transmission effect across generations was also significant. The estimate for habitual physical activity was 29%, and it was entirely attributable to genetic factors. The corresponding estimate for participation in moderate to vigorous physical activity was 12%, and it was accounted for by cultural transmission with no genetic effect. Since habitual physical activity was computed as the sum of all activities, and participation in moderate to vigorous activity

included only more vigorous activities, low intensity activities were probably those characterized by the significant genetic effect. The results were thus interpreted as an indication of inherited differences in the propensity to be spontaneously active or inactive (PÉRUSSE et al., 1989).

The energy cost associated with common body postures or positions (sitting or standing) and with low intensity activities (walking, bending, reaching, etc.) repeated several times in the course of a normal day may be an important determinant of the total daily energy expenditure. To test the hypothesis that such differences could be partly explained by genetic factors, the oxygen uptake required for various submaximal cycle ergometer workloads was measured in 22 pairs of male sedentary DZ twins and 31 pairs of male sedentary MZ twins, aged 16 to 29 years (BOUCHARD et al., 1989a). The correlations shown in Table 2 suggest a significant genetic effect for oxygen uptake per unit body weight at low power output (50, 75 and 100 watts). However, this effect became non-significant when energy expenditure reached about 6 times the resting metabolic rate. It is thus possible that there are inherited differences in the energy cost of low intensity activities even after adjustment for variation in body mass. The significance of this phenomenon for 24-hour energy expenditure remains to be investigated (Table 2).

Two studies have considered familial aggregation of 24-hour energy expenditure. RAVUSSIN et al., measured total daily energy expenditure in 94 siblings (52 males, 42 females) from 36 American Indian families (RAVUSSIN et al., 1988). After adjustment for age, sex and body

Table 2: Intraclass correlations for energy cost of submaximal steady-state cycle ergometer exercise

Power Output (W)	MZ twins VO₂/kg	DZ twins VO₂/kg
50	0.67**	0.22
75	0.72**	0.33*
100	0.82**	0.59**
125	0.79**	0.68**
150	0.75**	0.66**

*p < 0.05, **p < 0.001
Adapted from BOUCHARD et al., 1989a

composition, there was significant familial aggregation of 24-hour energy expenditure with 41% of the variance accounted for by family lines. In 71 healthy Caucasian siblings from 32 families, TOUBRO et al., (1996) reported intraclass familial correlation of 0.44 for sex-adjusted 24-hour energy expenditure.

2.2 Evidence from molecular studies
Molecular evidence for a genetic contribution to the regulation of physical activity level comes from neurological disorders in which either hyper- or hypo-activity is one of the clinical features. The dopamine (DA) transporter (DAT) and the DA receptors have been implicated in this context. DAT is expressed on the plasma membrane of dopaminergic neurons where it removes DA from the extracellular space and localizes it into the cytoplasm. The DAT knockout (KO) mice are lacking the transporter and thus are accumulating DA in the extracellular space of dopaminergic neurons. A prominent feature of these animals is their marked hyperactivity. For example, the DAT-KO mice show about a 12-fold higher locomotor activity in a novel environment than the wild-type animals (GAINET-DINOV et al., 1999). On the other hand, the D2 dopamine receptor (D2R) deficient mice exhibit markedly lower activity levels, quantified as the initiation of movement, time spent in motion, and horizontal distance traveled, than their strain-matched wild-type controls (KELLY et al., 1998). In addition to the D2R genotype, the genetic background of the animals influences the locomotor activity. This suggests that genetic factors besides the D2R locus influences the activity level regulation in these mice. Whether genetic variation at the DAT and D2R loci has any effect on the physical activity level in humans is unclear. However, both linkage and association studies in humans have indicated that the DAT locus is involved in the attention-deficient hyperactivity disorder (COOK et al., 1995; GILL et al., 1997; WALDMAN et al., 1998), which has hyperactivity as one of its clinical features.
Another example of the potential involvement of a gene in physical activity regulation comes from the fruit fly

(Drosophila melanogaster). These insects exhibit two distinct activity patterns related to food-search behaviour; rovers move about 2-times longer distances while feeding than sitters. This activity pattern is genetically determined and is regulated by the *dg2* gene, which encodes a cGMP-dependent protein kinase (PKG) (OSBORNE et al., 1997). PKG activity is significantly higher in wild-type rovers than in wild-type and mutant sitters and the activation of the *dg2* gene reverts foraging behaviour from a sitter to a rover. The role of the *dg2* gene in the regulation of food-search behaviour was confirmed by overexpressing the *dg2* gene in sitters, which resulted in a change of behavior to the rover phenotype.

These studies suggest that single genes can markedly influence physical activity-related behaviour in experimental models suggesting that it will perhaps be possible to undertake in the future the genetic dissection at the molecular level of habitual physical activity as a behavioural phenotype in humans.

3. Genetics of cardiorespiratory fitness

Several studies have provided evidence for the presence of marked interindividual differences in cardiorespiratory fitness phenotypes. This individual variability in fitness phenotypes has been described as a normal biological phenomenon which may reflect genetic diversity (BOUCHARD, 1995). For instance, it has been proposed that the higher concentrations of ATP and phosphocreatine at rest and during exercise, as well as the greater capacity for generation of ATP by oxidative metabolism during exer-

cise in the muscles not exposed to any specific exercise training program (wrist flexors) in world-class distance runners compared to sedentary controls is an indication of an underlying genetic endowment for physical endurance (PARK et al., 1988). This section will review the evidence accumulated on this topic for key phenotypes.

3.1 Evidence from genetic epidemiology studies

Maximal oxygen intake (VO₂max)
The heritability of VO_2max has been estimated from a few twin and family studies. Three family studies have measured VO_2max (BOUCHARD et al., 1998; BOUCHARD et al., 1986a; LESAGE et al., 1985). The most comprehensive of these is the HERITAGE Family Study, which is a multicenter study designed to investigate the role of the genotype in cardiovascular, metabolic and hormonal responses to aerobic exercise training (BOUCHARD et al., 1995). In 429 healthy but sedentary Caucasian subjects from 86 nuclear families, two maximal ergometer exercise tests were performed on separate days, with at least 48 hours between the tests (BOUCHARD et al., 1998). Respiratory gas exchange variables were directly measured in both tests and the average VO_2max from the two tests was used in the analyses if both values were within 5% of each other. If the difference was greater than 5%, the higher value was used. An analysis of variance revealed a clear familial aggregation of VO_2max in the sedentary state. The variance for VO_2max (adjusted for age, sex, body mass and body composition) was 2.72 times greater between families than within families and about 40% of the variance in VO_2max was

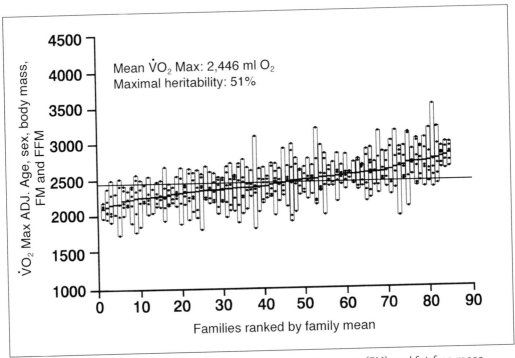

Figure 1: VO$_2$max adjusted (ADJ.) for age, sex, body mass, fat mass (FM) and fat-free mass (FFM) plotted by family rank. Each family is enclosed in a box, with individual data points plotted as dots and each family mean as a dash. The horizontal reference line is the group mean. Reproduced with permission from BOUCHARD et al. (1998): Medicine and Science in Sports and Exercise, 30, 252–258.

accounted for by family lines. Maximum likelihood estimation of familial correlations (spouse, four parent-offspring and three sibling correlations) revealed a maximal heritability (i. e. combined effect of genetic factors and nongenetic transmission) of 51% for VO$_2$max. However, the significant spouse correlation indicated that the genetic heritability was less than 50% (BOUCHARD et al., 1998). The concept of family lines with low and high VO$_2$max phenotypes in the sedentary state is illustrated in Figure 1. Table 3 summarizes intraclass correlations in pairs of DZ and MZ twins from 7 studies. The data vary in test protocol

(measured or predicted aerobic power, maximal or submaximal tests), the number of twin pairs, adjustment of data (uncontrolled age or sex effects), and differences in means or variances between twin types. The intraclass correlations for MZ twins ranged from about 0.6 to 0.9, whereas correlations for DZ twins with one exception ranged from 0.3 to 0.5. The largest of the twin studies (SUNDET et al., 1994) was derived from a population-based twin panel of conscripts. The data were based on predicted VO$_2$max values, which were subsequently transformed to categorical scores, from low to high maximal aerobic

Table 3: Intraclass correlations from twin studies for maximal oxygen intake

Source	N pairs		Phenotype	MZ	DZ
	MZ	DZ			
KLISSOURAS (1971): Males	15	10	VO_2max/kg	0.91	0.44
KLISSOURAS et al (1973): Males and Females	23	16	VO_2max/kg	0.95	0.36
BOUCHARD et al (1986a): Males and Females	53	33	VO_2max/kg	0.71	0.51
FAGARD et al (1991):	29	19	VO_2max/kg	0.77	0.04
MAES et al (1993): Males and Females	41	50	VO_2max/kg	0.85	0.56
SUNDET et al (1994): Males	436	622	VO_2max/kg Predicted[1])	0.62	0.29
MAES et al (1996): 10-year-old boys and girls	43	61	VO_2max[2])	0.75	0.32

[1]) Maximal aerobic power was predicted from a nomogram and the predicted VO_2max was subsequently transformed to a categorical score from 1 to 9. The intraclass correlations are based upon the categorical scores.
[2]) VO_2max not adjusted for body mass.

power, but intraclass correlations for the categorical scores were similar to those found in other twin studies (SUNDET et al., 1994).

In our own study involving 27 pairs of brothers, 33 pairs of dizygotic twins and 53 pairs of monozygotic twins (BOUCHARD et al., 1986a), heritability was about 40% for VO_2max per kg of body mass. However, since the correlation in dizygotic twins (intraclass = 0.51) was high in comparison to the brothers (intraclass = 0.71), we hypothesized that the 40% estimate was probably inflated by common environmental factors, and that the true heritability of VO_2max per kg of mass was more likely to lie between 25 and 40% of the adjusted phenotypic variance. In the same study, the total

power output during a 90 min maximal cycle ergometer test was also measured in 31 pairs of dizygotic and 33 pairs of monozygotic twins. The heritability for this test of endurance performance reached 60% when data were expressed per kg of body mass.

Statistical modelling approaches have been applied to estimate genetic and environmental sources of variation in VO_2max from twin data. For example, FAGARD and co-workers performed a path analysis of peak aerobic power in 29 MZ and 19 DZ pairs (FAGARD et al., 1991). The heritabilities of unadjusted peak work load, O_2 uptake and O_2 pulse were 81, 77 and 74%, respectively. When data were adjusted for body mass, skinfold thickness and sports participation, the heritability estimates were 80, 66 and 53%, respectively. Maes and collaborators applied structural equation modeling to data on 105 ten-year old twin pairs and their parents (97 mothers and 84 fathers) from the Leuven Longitudinal Twin Study (Maes et al., 1996). They quantified genetic and environmental sources of variation in several fitness components, including VO_2max measured during a maximal treadmill test. They observed a strong husband-wife correlation of 0.42 (N=79 pairs) for VO_2max (liters per min), markedly higher than in the HERITAGE Family Study (Bouchard et al., 1998). The results did not give a straightforward indication as to which of the models best explained the data. There was clear evidence for a strong genetic component to absolute VO_2max, but the genetic influence was reduced when VO_2max per kg of body mass was considered.

Maternal effects
Two familial studies have suggested the likelihood of a specific maternal effect for VO_2max (Lesage et al., 1985; Bouchard et al., 1998). This hypothesis was prompted by the observation that correlations reached 0.20 and above in mother-child pairs, but were about zero in father-child pairs for VO_2max per kg of mass or per kg of fat-free mass (Lesage et al., 1985). More recently, the HERITAGE Family Study (Bouchard et al., 1998) has also provided evidence for a substantial maternal heritability in VO_2max adjusted for age, sex, body mass and body composition. About half of the maximal heritability of VO_2max observed in the sedentary state was compatible with a maternal, and possibly a mitochondrial, transmission.

In contrast, no maternal effect was found in studies of submaximal power output (PWC_{150}/kg body weight) (Pérusse et al., 1988; Pérusse et al., 1987). Based on the father-offspring and mother-offspring correlations, the total transmissible variance for PWC_{150}/kg were 0.19 and 0.29, respectively, which were completely due to cultural inheritance without any effect of biological inheritance (Pérusse et al., 1987). There is also no consistent evidence that the transmission from parents to offspring is limited to one gender (boys or girls), although the additive genetic variance of absolute VO_2max was said to be stronger in girls than boys in the Leuven Longitudinal Twin Study (Maes et al., 1996).

Cardiac dimensions
Relative to their sedentary peers, endurance athletes have larger hearts, and larger stroke volumes and cardiac outputs during maximal exercise. They also show a resting bradycardia, and a slower heart rate at a given submaximal work rate. No genetic study on submaximal or maximal stroke volume and cardiac output has yet been reported. However, a few studies have addressed the issue of the heritability of heart size and cardiac dimensions.
Echographic measurements of cardiac dimensions in members of nuclear families suggest a familial resemblance in several ventricular dimensions (Adams et al., 1986; Thériault et al., 1986). Familial correlations among various kinds of relatives by descent and adoption were assessed for echocardiographically derived heart dimensions (Thériault et al., 1986). For most cardiac dimensions, correlations were significant in both biological relatives and relatives by

adoption, suggesting that both genetic and environmental factors contribute to the phenotypic variance.

In 32 MZ and 21 DZ pairs of healthy male twins (BIELEN et al., 1991a), a path analysis model was used to partition the phenotypic variance of left ventricular structure into genetic, shared environmental and non-shared environmental components. The data were adjusted for the effects of age and body mass. All heart structures, except left ventricular internal diameter, were significantly influenced by genetic factors, with heritability estimates ranging from 29% to 68%. The strong relationship between body size and cardiac dimensions raises the question of how much of the covariation between these two variables is explained by common genetic factors. This question was addressed in a bivariate genetic analysis of left ventricular mass and body mass in 147 MZ and 107 DZ pubertal twin pairs of both sexes (VERHAAREN et al., 1991). Heritabilities of left ventricular mass reached 60% in males and 73% in females. After adjustment of left ventricular mass for body mass and sexual maturity, the genetic effect was reduced but remained significant, with heritabilities of 39% and 59% in males and females, respectively. Bivariate genetic analyses showed that the correlation between left ventricular mass and body mass was almost entirely of genetic origin, 90% being attributed to common genes (VERHAAREN et al., 1991). These studies suggest that genetic factors are important in determining cardiac dimensions under resting conditions. One study considered the inheritance of cardiac changes during submaximal supine cycle exercise at a heart rate of 110 beats per minute of 21 MZ and 12 DZ twin pairs (BIELEN et al., 1991b). The increases of left ventricular internal diameter and fractional shortening in response to exercise showed genetic effects of 24% and 47%, respectively. The results were interpreted as an indication that adaptation of cardiac function during submaximal exercise may be partly determined by the genotype (BIELEN et al., 1991b).

Exercise blood pressure

In addition to resting blood pressure (HAMET et al., 1998), genetic factors have been implicated also in determining blood pressure responses to a variety of physical, mental, behavioral and biological stimuli. Evidence from twin and family studies suggest that blood pressure "reactivity" is genetically conditioned (PICKERING et al., 1994). For example, a segregation analysis study of 864 subjects from 81 pedigrees showed a mixed recessive model of transmission for diastolic blood pressure response to a cycle ergometer exercise test, with a putative gene frequency of 0.21. The phenotypic variance explained by the major gene and polygenic effects were 33.6% and 16.6%, respectively (CHENG et al., 1997). In a cohort of 148 MZ and 111 DZ twin pairs with a mean age of 11.1 years, significant genetic effects were found for heart rate and blood pressures measured during a bicycle ergometer test (BREE et al., 1996). Furthermore, the results suggested that the genetic effects found at rest influenced also the exercise phenotypes, although the effect tended to decline with increasing exercise intensity. In addition, the exercise specific genetic effects increased for all three traits as a function of the exercise work load.

Muscle mass and size

The muscle size as well as the number and type of muscle fibers contribute significantly to muscle force production. Results from twin studies suggest that genetic factors have a major effect both on midarm and paraspinal muscle cross-sectional areas (CSA) (THOMIS et al., 1997; GIBBONS et al., 1998). In 25 pairs of MZ twins and 16 pairs of DZ twins, aged 17–30 years (all males), Thomis and co-workers reported a correlation of 0.81 for mean midarm-muscle CSA derived from computed tomography scans in MZ twins whereas no correlation ($r = -0.01$) was observed in DZ twins (THOMIS et al., 1997). The contribution of genetic factors to the midarm-muscle CSA variation was 92% and unique environmental factors explained the remaining 8%. Moreover, the multivariate analysis revealed that one common genetic factor explained a major part of the covariation between the midarm muscle CSA and isometric strength measured at three elbow angles (THOMIS et al., 1997).

In a study of 65 pairs of Finnish male MZ twins, aged 35 to 65 years, it is of interest to note that, despite the limitations associated with the use of only MZ twins in a cross-sectional design, the heritability was the strongest determinant of paraspinal muscle cross-sectional area measured by magnetic resonance imaging (GIBBONS et al., 1998). Familial aggregation explained 69%, 73% and 66% of the variance in the age-adjusted cross-sectional area of the erector spinae, psoas major and quadratus lumborum muscles, respectively. Levels of self-reported occupational, sport, and leisure-time physical activities had only negligible effects (GIBBONS et al., 1998).Finally, based on a small number of MZ (n = 5) and DZ (n = 7) twin pairs, genetic effects of 93.9% and 82.4% were estimated for the left and right maximal masseter muscle cross-sections, respectively, measured by magnetic resonance imaging (LAUWERYNS et al., 1995).

Skeletal muscle tissue is the major component of fat-free mass (FFM), and both twin and family studies indicate a significant genetic contribution to FFM. In a cohort of 706 postmenopausal women, including 227 pairs of MZ twins and 126 pairs of DZ twins, lean body mass was measured by dual-energy X-ray absorptiometry (DXA). The results yielded a heritability estimate of 0.52 for lean body mass (ARDEN, SPECTOR, 1997). Two Australian studies, one based on data from 56 MZ and 56 DZ female twin pairs aged 24 to 67 years (SEEMAN et al., 1996), and the other using data from 20 to 83 years old MZ (n = 57) and DZ (n = 55) female twin pairs (NGUYEN et al., 1998), reported that genetic factors explained 87% and 83.5%, respectively, of the variance in lean body mass derived from DXA measurements.

In the Quebec Family Study, path analysis of familial correlations computed among various pairs of relatives by descent or adoption indicated a total transmissible variance of 40% to 50% for FFM with a genetic effect accounting for about 30% of the variance (BOUCHARD et al., 1988a). Subsequent commingling analysis of these data has shown that FFM was characterized by a single distribution in parents but not in the offspring (BORECKI et al., 1991). However, segregation analysis of the data did not provide evidence for a major locus effect on FFM (RICE et al., 1993). In contrast, about 60% of the variance in FFM was accounted for by a non-Mendelian major effect, which may reflect environmentally based commingling or which may be, in part, a function of gene-environment interactions or correlations (RICE et al., 1993). It may be inferred, therefore, that some undetermined genetic characteristics contribute to individuality in estimated muscle mass.

Muscle fiber type distribution
The limited data on the extent to which human skeletal muscle fiber types are under the control of genetic factors have provided variable results. An early twin study on a small sample of MZ (n = 15 pairs) and DZ (n = 16 pairs) twins yielded surprisingly high heritability coefficients for the proportion of type I fibers in the vastus lateralis, 0.995 in males and 0.928 in females (KOMI et al., 1977). However, data from a larger series of twins and siblings indicate markedly lower estimates of heritability. In a cohort of 32 pairs of brothers, 26 pairs of DZ and 35 pairs of male and female MZ twins, intraclass correlations for the proportion of different fibers in the vastus lateralis yielded heritability estimates ranging from 66% (twice the biological sibship correlation) to 55% (directly from the MZ twin sibships correlation) to 6% (twice the difference between MZ and DZ correlations) (BOUCHARD et al., 1986b; BOUCHARD et al., 1992). Although brothers and DZ twins share about one-half of their genes by descent, comparison of the respective within pair correlations suggests that increased environmental similarity, i.e., DZ twins experience more similar environmental circumstances than brothers separated in age, translates into increased phenotypic resemblance for the proportion of type I fibers.

There was no indication of a genetic effect in type IIA fiber proportion, but more resemblance within MZ twin pairs for type IIB fibers was observed than within DZ twin and sibling pairs. Estimated heritabilities of type I fiber proportion in the vastus lateralis muscle from different studies (BOUCHARD et al., 1986b; KOMI et al., 1977) are thus widely divergent, ranging from a low of 6% to a high of almost 100%. Allowing for sampling and technical variation, it appears that factors other than the genotype are involved in the modulation of the proportions of type I and type II fibers in the vastus lateralis muscle. Nevertheless, the variability in the percentage of type I fibers within specific pairs of twins suggests that there are genetic factors which predispose some individuals to have a high or low percentage of type I or type II fibers. Based on 35 pairs of MZ twins, the mean difference in percentage of type I fibers between a member of an MZ pair and his/her co-twin control reached 9.5 + 6.9% (SIMONEAU, BOUCHARD, 1995). The difference in the percentage of type I fibers between members of a MZ pair was less than 6% in 16 pairs and the largest difference was 23%, which was observed in three pairs, and was of the same magnitude as the largest differences when samples were taken from the right and left vastus lateralis of the same individual (SIMONEAU, BOUCHARD, 1995). Taken together, the results of human and animal studies (NAKAMURA et al., 1993; NIMMO et al., 1985) led to the suggestion that a genetic component accounts for about 40% to 50% of the variation in the proportion of type I muscle fibers in humans (Figure 2) (SIMONEAU, BOUCHARD, 1995).

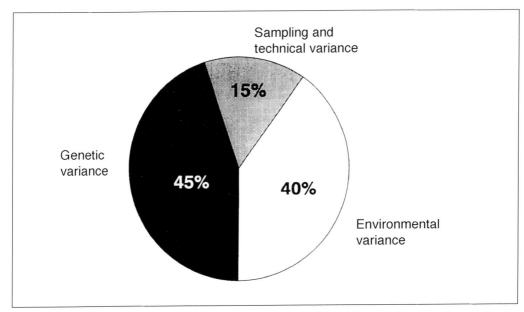

Figure 2: Estimates of the sampling and technical, environmental, and genetic variances for the proportion of type I fibers in human skeletal muscle. Reproduced with permission from Simoneau, J. A.; BOUCHARD, C. (1995): Genetic determinism of fiber type proportion in human skeletal muscle. FASEB Journal, 9, 1091–1095.

Metabolic properties of skeletal muscle
There is considerable variation among individuals in the enzymatic activity profile of skeletal muscle. There are high and low activity levels of enzyme markers of the catabolism of different substrates in the skeletal muscle of healthy sedentary and moderately active individuals of both sexes (SIMONEAU, BOUCHARD, 1995). Many factors probably contribute to this variation among individuals, and it is likely that the genotype plays a role in the amount of protein for several important metabolic enzymes of skeletal muscle.

Data on the extent of genetic determination of enzyme activity markers in skeletal muscle are limited. Earlier studies based on small samples of MZ and DZ twins (HOWALD, 1976; KOMI et al.,

1977) suggested no gene-associated variation in several enzyme activities. However, data for a larger sample of MZ (n = 35) and DZ (n=26) twins of both sexes and pairs of biological brothers (n = 32) indicated that variation in several key enzymes of skeletal muscle was inherited to a significant extent (Table 4). There was a significant within pair resemblance in MZ twins for all skeletal muscle enzyme activities (r = 0.30 to 0.68), but the within pair correlations for DZ twins and brothers suggest that variation in several enzyme activities were related to non-genetic factors and environmental conditions. Nevertheless, after adjusting for the age and sex effects, it appears that genetic factors are responsible for about 25% to 50% of the total phenotypic variation in the

Table 4: Intraclass coefficients for enzyme activities in the vastus lateralis muscle of twins and brothers

Enzyme	MZ (n = 35)	DZ (n = 26)	Brothers (n = 32)
Creatine kinase (CK)	0.61**	0.53**	–
Hexokinase (HK)	0.41**	0.75**	−0.22
Phosphofructokinase (PFK)	0.55**	0.35*	0.27
Lactate dehydrogenase (LDH)	0.68**	0.03	0.50**
Malate dehydrogenase (MDH)	0.58**	−0.14	0.15
Oxoglutarate dehydrogenase (OGDH)	0.53**	0.19	0.09
2-hydroxyacyl CoA dehydrogenase (HADH)	0.43**	−0.33	0.48*
PFK/OGDH ratio	0.30*	0.06	0.34*

$^*p < 0.05$, $^{**}p < 0.01$
Adapted from Bouchard et al., 1986b

activities of the regulatory enzymes of the glycolytic (phosphofructokinase, PFK) and citric acid cycle (oxoglutarate dehydrogenase, OGDH) pathways, and of the variation in the ratio of glycolytic to oxidative activities (PFK/OGDH ratio) (BOUCHARD et al., 1986b). Such genetic effects could not be accounted for by charge variation in the enzyme proteins (BOUCHARD et al., 1988b, MARCOTTE et al., 1987); they likely depend upon individual differences in transcription rate or translation.

3.2 Evidence from molecular studies
The evidence from the genetic epidemiology studies reviewed above suggest that there is a genetically determined component affecting cardiorespiratory fitness phenotypes. However, since this trait is complex and multifactorial in nature, the search for genes and mutations responsible for the genetic regulation must not only target several families of phenotypes but also consider the phenotypes in the sedentary state and in

response to exercise training. Most of the studies available are based on the candidate gene approach and only one preliminary linkage study has been reported in humans, using a limited number of markers on one chromosome only (GAGNON et al., 1997). Here, we review the evidence for a role of selected candidate genes and mitochondrial DNA on VO₂max and other relevant phenotypes based on the data from cross-sectional studies. However, it must be emphasized that for some of the candidate genes of skeletal muscle phenotypes the review is based mainly on animal studies and, thus, the applicability to humans is unknown. The results of candidate gene studies in relation to the training response are presented later in the chapter.

Angiotensin-converting enzyme (ACE)
Over the last two years, some studies have reported significant associations between an ACE insertion/deletion (I/D) polymorphism and performance related

phenotypes. In a case-control study of 64 Australian olympic level rowers and 114 non-athlete controls, higher frequencies of the I allele and the I/I genotype were observed in athletes (0.57 and 0.30, respectively) than in controls (0.43 and 0.18, respectively) (GAYAGAY et al., 1998). In a group of 25 British male mountaineers, who had a history of ascending beyond 7000 meters without using supplementary oxygen, a relative excess of the I allele and a deficiency of the D allele was reported, as compared to 1906 British males free from clinical cardiovascular disease (MONTGOMERY et al., 1998). Finally, the relationship between ACE I/D polymorphism and VO_2max was investigated in three groups of postmenopausal women with low (sedentary, n = 19), moderate (physically active, n = 19) or high (athletes, n = 20) level of habitual physical activity (HAGBERG et al., 1998). In all physical activity subgroups, women with the I/I genotype had the highest VO_2max value and, in the pooled data, the differences between genotypes were statistically significant. However, both the genotype and the allele frequencies were similar across the physical activity subgroups.

Although the results seem to support the hypothesis of an association between a high cardiorespiratory fitness and the I allele of the ACE I/D polymorphism, the small number of subjects and the design of these studies are of concern. In collaboration with European laboratories (Freiburg, Germany and Kuopio, Finland) and a center from the USA (Dallas, TX), we have established a DNA bank of more than 350 Caucasian male endurance athletes with VO_2max exceeding 75 ml/kg/min along with sedentary control subjects with VO_2max less than 50 ml/kg/min (the GENEATHLETE cohort). Based on the data from 173 athletes and 197 controls, no differences were found in the distribution of the ACE I/D genotypes between the two groups (WOLFARTH B. et al., personal communication). Further classification of the athletes based on measured VO_2max did not provide any evidence for an excess of the I allele or the I/I genotype among the athletes with extremely high VO_2max level (> 85 ml/kg/min). Similarly, in 476 Caucasian and 248 Black subjects from the HERITAGE Family Study cohort, no associations were observed between cardiorespiratory fitness phenotypes measured in the sedentary state and the ACE I/D polymorphism (RANKINEN et al., 1999a).

Considering the negative findings from these larger studies and the lack of a plausible physiological explanation for an association between the cardiorespiratory fitness phenotypes and the ACE polymorphism, it is unlikely that DNA sequence variation in the ACE gene is a major determinant of cardiorespiratory endurance in humans.

Erythropoietin receptor (EPOR)
Another potential candidate gene is the erythropoietin receptor (EPOR) encoded on chromosome 19p13.3–p13.2. An adequate oxygen delivery to skeletal muscles and other tissues is required to sustain a high endurance performance. Erythropoietin is a cytokine which regulates the proliferation and differentiation of erythroid precursor cells thus influencing the red blood cell levels and ultimately the oxygen transport capacity. Its effect is mediated by the EPOR and several mutations in exon 8 of the EPOR gene have been shown to produce trun-

cated receptors missing the C-terminal negative regulatory domain (DE LA CHAPELLE et al., 1993; SOKOL et al., 1995; ARCASOY et al., 1997; KRALOVICS et al., 1997). These mutations have been shown to be responsible for familial erythrocytosis, an autosomal dominant inherited disorder which is characterized by increased red blood cell mass. The observation that in the first study reporting a linkage between the EPOR gene and familial erythrocytosis (JUVONEN et al., 1991), one of the family members was a world-class cross-country skier and had won several olympic gold medals and world championships, led to the hypothesis that some EPOR mutations may predispose to enhanced endurance performance (LONGMORE, 1993).

The associations between elite endurance athlete status and EPOR gene polymorphisms were investigated in 215 athletes and 201 sedentary controls from the GENEATHLETE cohort (WOLFARTH B. et al., unpublished observations). Three microsatellite markers were typed at the EPOR gene locus. The number of carriers of the 185 bp allele of a tetranucleotide repeat marker in the untranslated 5' region of the gene was significantly greater ($p = 0.002$) in athletes than in controls. A trend for a significant difference ($p = 0.044$) between endurance athletes and controls was also seen for the frequency of a 205 bp fragment. Even though more studies of this gene are needed, these results suggest that the EPOR gene may play a role in the endurance performance of Caucasian males.

Mitochondrial DNA (mtDNA)
Because of the apparent maternal effect on VO_2max (BOUCHARD et al., 1998; LESAGE et al., 1985), mtDNA is of particular interest as it is inherited from the maternal oocyte. The human mtDNA is a circular duplex molecule of 16,569 bp that does not recombine and is self-replicative. mtDNA contains no introns and it codes for 13 of the 67 polypeptides involved in the respiratory chain and oxidative phosphorylation, plus two ribosomal and 22 transfer RNAs. The displacement-loop (D-loop) region is a noncoding segment that contains the promoters for transcription of heavy and light mtDNA strands, the origin of replication of the heavy strand, and conserved sequences essential for the mtDNA expression (CLAYTON, 1982; GREENBERG et al., 1983). The mitochondrial genome thus contains good candidate genes for endurance performance. mtDNA sequence variation was investigated using RFLP technology in sedentary subjects submitted to endurance training (DIONNE et al., 1991). Carriers of three mtDNA morphs, one due to a base change in the tRNA for threonine and two others caused by base substitutions in the subunit 5 of the NADH dehydrogenase (MTND5) gene, had a body-mass adjusted VO_2max in the untrained state significantly higher than that found in noncarriers. A lower response of VO_2max to endurance training was also observed for three carriers of a variant in MTND5. A MTND5-NciI polymorphism at bp 13,364, a BamHI marker at bp 13,470 and a D-loop KpnI variant at bp 16,133 were assessed in 125 endurance athletes from the GENATHLETE cohort and in a group of matched controls (RIVERA et al., 1998). The MTND5-NciI variant was found in 12.9% of the athletes and 14% of controls, and the MTND5-BamHI variant was observed in 12.8% of endurance athletes and 12.3% of sedentary

controls. The frequency of the D-loop KpnI mutation was 5.8% in athletes and 1.6% in controls. As frequencies of these polymorphisms were not different between athletes and controls, it was concluded that these three mtDNA poly-morphisms were not associated with athletic performance. However, it cannot be excluded that some mtDNA variants may have functional implications for the cardiorespiratory endurance of seden-tary subjects and yet no be longer impor-tant in elite endurance athletes. For instance, the mitochondrial content of skeletal muscle may play a major role in sedentary subjects (i. e., those with a high content may have a higher VO_2max), whereas cardiovascular parameters or other factors may account for a more significant fraction of the variance in VO_2max between endurance athletes and sedentary people.

AMP deaminase
AMP deaminase catalyzes the deamina-tion of AMP to IMP and ammonia. It has been suggested that the AMP deaminase offsets the exercise-induced decrease in the ATP/ADP ratio by clearing skeletal muscle AMP and thereby directing the myokinase reaction toward ATP resyn-thesis. This would ease the inhibitory effect of a low ATP/ADP ratio on muscle contraction. Among patients with an AMP deaminase deficiency, one-half show impaired exercise capacity due to muscle cramps, pain and early fatigue. The skeletal muscle AMP deaminase activity is strongly influenced by the muscle-specific AMP deaminase (AMPD1) genotype. The homozygotes for a nonsense mutation in exon 2 of the AMPD1 gene exhibit very low enzyme activities (< 15 mmol/min/kg dry mass)

whereas the values for the wild-type homozygotes range from 1000 to 2250 mmol/min/kg dry mass (NORMAN et al., 1998a). However, among 18 healthy subjects, no differences were observed in a short-term, high-intensity exercise performance (30 s sprint on a cycle ergo-meter) between the AMPD1 genotypes, although the concentration of ATP decreased by 40% and that of IMP increased by 234 % in the vastus lateralis muscle during the test in the wild-type homozygotes (n = 7) whereas no change was evident in the homozygotes for the mutant allele (n = 4) (NORMAN et al., 1998b). Thus, the role of this AMPD1 polymorphism on short-term maximal performance capacity remains to be confirmed in future studies with larger sample sizes.

Growth hormone
Genes affecting the production of anabolic hormones are potential candi-dates for the regulation of muscle mass and muscular strength. Introduction of human or rat growth hormone gene into mice resulted in elevated serum growth hormone levels and transgenic animals grew significantly larger than control mice (PALMITER et al., 1982; PALMITER et al., 1983). Similarly, transgenic mouse carrying the coding regions of the bovine growth hormone (bGH) gene, which was expressed in liver and kidneys but not in the skeletal muscle, showed markedly increased serum bGH and insulin-like growth factor I levels (WOLF et al., 1995). The forelimb and hindlimb muscle weights were also significantly greater than in the non-transgenic littermates. However, despite a greater muscle mass, a greater absolute grip strength was observed only in transgenic females.

Moreover, when the grip strength was expressed relative to body weight, the transgenic animals showed significantly lower levels than controls. Although the growth hormone therapy seems to have benefical effects on muscle mass and strength in patients with GH deficiency (CUNEO et al., 1991; JANSSEN et al., 1999), the data on transgenic mice, together with the observations that a GH treatment has no effect on muscle growth and performance during a resistance training program (YARASHESKI et al., 1992; DEYSSIG et al., 1993; YARASHESKI et al., 1993; TAAFFE et al., 1994; YARASHESKI et al., 1995; TAAFFE et al., 1996; ZACHWIEJA et al., 1996) cast doubts over the hypothesis that the human GH gene has a major effect on muscular strength in healthy subjects with normal GH levels. However, it must be remembered that studies on the associations between DNA sequence variation at the human GH gene locus and skeletal muscle mass or performance are missing at the moment.

Myostatin
In addition to anabolic hormones, various growth and differentiation factors are potential candidates for the genetic regulation of muscle mass. Myostatin belongs to the transforming growth factor β superfamily, is expressed in developing and adult skeletal muscle and functions as a negative regulator of skeletal muscle mass. Gene targeting experiments have shown that mice lacking the myostatin gene have a 2- to 3-fold increase in muscle size due to an increased number of muscle fibers (McPHERRON et al., 1997). Body fat content of the mutant mice is normal. Similar phenotypes to myostatin null

mice have been known to occur naturally in several cattle breeds and recently it was shown that the double muscling in cattle is caused by a frameshift mutation in the myostatin gene which eliminates the active region of the molecule (McPHERRON, LEE, 1997; GROBET et al., 1997). This is the first proof of a naturally occuring single-gene mutation with profound effect on skeletal muscle size. There are no data available on the functional properties of the muscles in myostatin-deficient animals. However, unlike the transgenic growth hormone animals, the animals with a myostatin gene mutation are viable and healthy and they seem to tolerate well the increased muscle mass, with the possible exception that the pregnant animals may experience problems during late gestation and at parturition. Studies on the myostatin gene in humans are lacking.

Ski gene
Another example of a growth regulating gene is the ski gene, which encodes a nuclear protein that binds to DNA in association with other cellular factors and modulates transcription and thereby may regulate tissue growth. Overexpression of *ski* in skeletal muscle of transgenic mice leads to substantial increases in muscle size (SUTRAVE et al., 1990). For example, the cross-sectional area of the plantaris muscle in mature male transgenic animals is 3.5-times greater than in controls. The increase in muscle mass is due to the selective hypertrophy of type II fibers but the number of fibers is similar to that of wild-type control animals. Transgenic animals have also a very low level of body fat and there are some evidence of skeletal abnormalities, possibly as an adaptation to increased

muscle mass. On the other hand, mice lacking the ski gene show developmental defects in several tissues, including skeletal muscle (BERK et al., 1997). No study on the ski gene and human skeletal muscle phenotypes has been reported yet.

4. Genetics of responsiveness to exercise training

Several exercise training studies have shown that there are marked interindividual differences in the trainability of cardiorespiratory endurance phenotypes after exposure to an identical training program (BOUCHARD, 1983). As illustrated in Figure 3, after a supervised trai-

ning program of 20 weeks in 476 healthy but sedentary Caucasian subjects of the HERITAGE Family Study, the training responses of VO$_2$max ranged from almost no change to an increase of almost one liter (BOUCHARD et al., 1999). Similarly, the improvements in total work output during a 90-min ergometer test ranged from 16 to 97 percent after 20 weeks of standardized endurance training in a separate experiment (LORTIE et al., 1984). Are genetic factors involved in these individual differences in responsiveness to exercise training? Although the data are not extensive, the results from genetic epidemiology studies and molecular markers support the hypothesis that the response to exercise training is partly modulated by genetic factors.

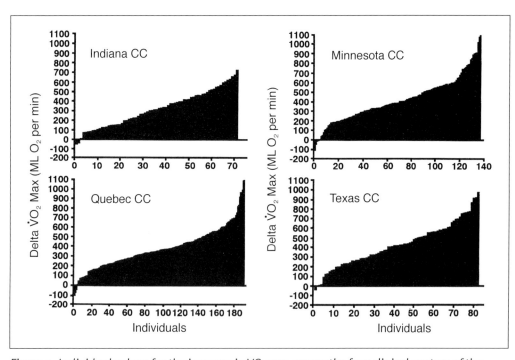

Figure 3: Individual values for the increase in VO$_2$max across the four clinical centers of the HERITAGE Family Study in response to a 20-week endurance training program. Reproduced with permission from BOUCHARD et al. (to be completed).

Genetic Aspects of Physical Activity

4.1 Evidence from genetic epidemiology studies

Cardiorespiratory fitness phenotypes

We believe that the main cause of the heterogeneity in training response is related to as yet undetermined genetic characteristics. To test this hypothesis, we have performed training studies with pairs of monozygotic twins, the rationale being that the response pattern will be more similar for individuals having the same genotype (within pairs) than for subjects with different genotypes (between pairs). Results from these twin studies and data from the HERITAGE Family Study suggest that the trainability of cardiorespiratory fitness phenotypes is, to some extent, genetically determined. The results of these studies are reviewed in this section.

In pairs of MZ twins, the VO_2max response to standardized training in a series of experiments showed 6 to 9 times more variance between genotypes (between pairs of twins) than within genotypes (within pairs of twins) (BOUCHARD et al., 1992). The similarity of training response among members of MZ twin pairs is illustrated in Figure 4. In this particular experiment, 10 pairs of male MZ twins were submitted to a standardized endurance training program for 20 weeks. Gains in absolute VO_2max showed almost 8 times more variance between than within pairs of twins. The intrapair resemblance for changes in VO_2max were significant with an intraclass correlation reaching 0.77 (PRUD'HOMME et al., 1984; BOUCHARD et al., 1992).

A related measure of aerobic performance is the total work output during a prolonged exercise bout. In 6 pairs of MZ twins, the total power output during a 90

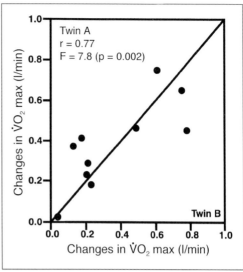

Figure 4: Intrapair resemblance (intraclass coefficients) in 10 pairs of monozygotic twins for training changes in VO₂max (liters of O₂ per min) after 20 weeks of endurance training. Reproduced with permission from BOUCHARD, C.; DIONNE, F. T.; SIMONEAU, J. A.; BOULAY, M. R. (1992): Genetics of aerobic and anaerobic performances. In: Exercise and Sport Sciences Reviews, 20, 27–58.

minute maximal cycle ergometer test was monitored before and after 15 weeks of endurance training (HAMEL et al., 1986). The resemblance in total power output within twin pairs was significant (intraclass r = 0.83), and the ratio of between pairs to within pairs variances was about 11.

The most convincing evidence for the presence of family lines in the trainability of VO_2max comes from the HERITAGE Family Study. The adjusted (age, sex and baseline VO_2max) VO_2max response showed 2.6 times more variance between families than within families, and the model-fitting analytical procedure yielded a maximal heritability esti-

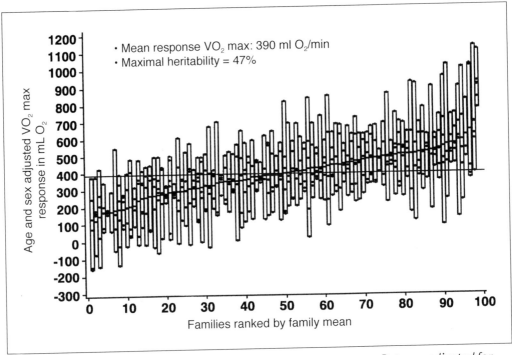

Figure 5: VO₂max response to a 20-week endurance training program. Data are adjusted for age, sex and pre-training VO₂max plotted by family rank. Each family is enclosed in a box, with individual data points plotted as dots and each family mean as a dash. The horizontal reference line is the group mean. Reproduced with permission from BOUCHARD et al. (to be completed).

mate of 47% (BOUCHARD et al., 1999). The familial aggregation of the VO₂max response phenotype is illustrated in Figure 5.

The physiological determinants of endurance performance also show genotype-training interactions. A cohort of 10 pairs of sedentary MZ twins were submitted to a 20-week program of endurance-training on a cycle ergometer and changes in cardiac dimensions were assessed by echocardiography (LANDRY et al., 1985). Despite the absence of significant changes in heart dimensions with exercise training, the within-pair resemblance was greater after training than before, suggesting that the variability of the response of cardiac dimensions to endurance training was potentially influenced by undetermined genes.

Skeletal muscle phenotypes
The evidence for potential genotypic contributions to the response of skeletal muscle metabolic characteristics to training comes from three studies on young adult MZ twins. All three included male and female MZ twins, and the gains associated with the respective training programs were similar in both sexes. In one study, the training program involved both continuous and interval work on a

cycle ergometer for 15 weeks in 12 pairs of MZ twins of both sexes. Although there were significant changes in the proportions of type I and type IIB fibers, the intraclass correlations showed no significant within pair resemblance for fiber type proportions. The responses of all enzymes except PFK and 2-hydroxy-acyl CoA dehydrogenase (HADH) were at least three times more similar within MZ pairs than between pairs. The evidence suggests that about 50% to 60% of the training responses in hexokinase (HK), lactate dehydrogenase (LDH), malate dehydrogenase (MDH), OGDH and the PFK/OGDH ratio in response to the inter-mittent training program were asso-ciated with the genotype; about 80% of the training response in creatine kinase (CK) appeared to be determined by the genotype (SIMONEAU et al., 1986).

In a second study of four pairs of young adult MZ twins (1 pair of males, 3 pairs of females), the response of skeletal muscle OGDH activity to a 10 week isoki-netic strength training appeared to be significantly genotype-dependent. The responses of CK and HADH to training seemed to be less genotype-dependent, as reflected by the lower genotype-trai-ning interaction F ratios (THIBAULT et al., 1986). These results emphasize the need for further study of the genetic basis of the response of skeletal muscle to strength training.

The third study followed six pairs of young adult MZ twins (3 males and 3 females) through 15 weeks of ergocycle endurance training (HAMEL et al., 1986). Genotype training interactions were evaluated for the proportion of muscle fibers and several enzymes after 7 weeks and after 15 weeks of training. Relative changes in the proportions of type I and type IIA and IIB fibers were not signifi-cant. More importantly, there was no significant genotype-training interaction effect (i.e., intra-pair resemblance in response to training) for the distribution of fiber types. The responses of skeletal muscle tissue enzyme activities observed during the first half of training were not related to the genotype, with the exception of that in PFK activity. However, during the second part of the training program, changes in the activi-ties of PFK, MDH, HADH and OGDH were partly determined by the genotype as evidenced by the significant intraclass correlations. Thus, within pair similarity in the response of skeletal muscle enzyme activities apparently varies with time during a training program. This in turn suggests that adaptation to endu-rance training early in a program may be under less stringent genetic control; however, as training continues and perhaps approaches maximal trainabi-lity, the response to training could be more genotype dependent.

Body composition
The genotype effects for the responses of body composition phenotypes to endurance training were investigated in seven pairs of young adult male MZ twins who completed a negative energy balance protocol during which they exer-cised on cycle ergometers twice a day, 9 out of 10 days, over a period of 93 days while being kept on a constant daily energy and nutrient intake (BOUCHARD et al., 1994b). The mean total energy deficit caused by exercise below the estimated energy cost of body weight maintenance reached 58,000 kcal. Mean body weight loss was 5.0 kg and was entirely accounted for by the loss of fat mass.

Table 5: Effect of an exercise training induced negative energy balance in MZ twins on body weight and composition and intrapair resemblance in response (Mean SEM)

	Training response	F-ratio	Intraclass coefficient
Body weight, kg	-5.0 ± 0.6***	6.8*	0.74*
Body Mass Index, kg/m^2	-1.6 ± 0.2***	6.1*	0.72*
Fat Mass, kg	-4.9 ± 0.6***	14.1**	0.87**
Fat-Free Mass, kg	-0.1 ± 0.3	8.2**	0.78**
Percent fat, %	-4.8 ± 0.6***	9.0**	0.80**
Body Energy, MJ	-191 ± 24***	12.9**	0.86**
Sum of 10 Skinfolds, mm	-52 ± 7**	11.8**	0.84**
Abdominal Visceral Fat, cm^2	-29 ± 3***	11.7**	0.84**

* $P \leq 0.05$, ** $P \leq 0.01$, *** $P \leq 0.001$
Adapted from BOUCHARD. et al., 1994b

Subcutaneous fat loss was slightly more pronounced on the trunk than on the limbs as estimated from skinfolds, circumferences and computed tomography. The reduction in abdominal visceral fat area was quite striking, from 81 cm^2 to 52 cm^2. At the same submaximal power output level, subjects oxidized more lipids than carbohydrates after the program as indicated by changes in the respiratory exchange ratio.

Intrapair resemblance was observed for the changes in body weight, fat mass, percent body fat, body energy content, sum of 10 skinfolds, abdominal visceral fat, and respiratory exchange ratio during submaximal work, with F-ratios and intraclass correlations ranging from 6.1 to 14.1 and 0.72 to 0.87, respectively (Table 5). Even though there were large individual differences in response to the negative energy balance and exercise protocol, subjects with the same genotype were more alike in responses than subjects with different genotypes parti-

cularly for body fat, body energy and abdominal visceral fat changes. High lipid oxidizers and low lipid oxidizers during submaximal exercise were also seen despite the fact that all subjects had experienced the same exercise and nutritional conditions for about three months.

Thus, changes in body mass, body fat, and body energy content are characterized by more heterogeneity between twin pairs than within pairs. These results are remarkably similar to those reported earlier for body mass, body fat and body energy gains with 12 pairs of twins subjected to a 100-day overfeeding protocol (BOUCHARD et al., 1990).

4.2 Evidence from molecular studies

Angiotensinogen (AGT) and angiotensin-converting enzyme (ACE)

Only a few candidate genes have been tested so far in the context of the training responsiveness to endurance exercise. In a series of reports based on a cohort of young British male military recruits, significant associations were reported between the ACE I/D polymorphism and training responses of cardiac phenotypes, muscular endurance performance and body composition (MONTGOMERY et al., 1997; MONTGOMERY et al., 1998; MONTGOMERY et al., 1999). Following a 10-week military training period, the D/D homozygotes of the ACE polymorphism showed significant increases in cardiac septal and posterior wall thicknesses and in left ventricular mass, whereas no changes were evident in the I/I homozygotes (MONTGOMERY et al., 1997). Later, it was reported that the increase in a number of repetitive elbow flexions with a 15-kg barbell was 11-fold greater in the I/I homozygotes than in the D/D homozygotes (MONTGOMERY et al., 1998), and that the increases in fat mass and non-fat mass, assessed using the bioimpedance method were greater in men with the I/I genotype as compared to those carrying the D allele (MONTGOMERY et al., 1999). Considering the physiological role of the ACE, the results on the responses of cardiac dimensions seem biologically plausible. However, the lack of a reasonable mechanism for the latter two associations, as well as the questionable validity and repeatability of the performance test used, raise doubts over these results.

In the HERITAGE Family Study cohort, we analyzed the associations between the ACE I/D polymorphism and the training responses of fitness-related phenotypes (O_2 consumption, power output, heart rate, cardiac output, stroke volume, minute ventilation, tidal volume, blood lactate level) at maximal and submaximal exercise in 476 Caucasian and 248 Black subjects (RANKINEN et al., 1999a).

No evidence was found to support a greater training responsiveness of the subjects with the I/I genotype. Out of the 108 association tests performed on 27 phenotypes in 4 groups of participants, only 9 showed significant p-values. In contrast to previous claims, in Caucasian offspring the D/D homozygotes showed the greatest increases in VO_2 and power output phenotypes and decreases in heart rate at submaximal exercise at a constant power output (50 W). No associations were evident in Caucasian parents or in Black parents or offspring. Further analyses with the body composition phenotype responses yielded also negative findings.

Thus, the data from the HERITAGE Family Study, based on well controlled and standardized phenotype measurements, a large sample size and a carefully monitored and standardized training protocol, do not support the hypothesis that the ACE I/D polymorphism plays a major role in cardiorespiratory endurance.

The renin-angiotensin system (RAS) is involved in the regulation of blood pressure. Angiotensin II, the active endproduct of RAS, is a powerful vasoconstrictor and it increases renal sodium and fluid reabsorption by stimulating the release of aldosterone. Among the individual components of RAS, the genes encoding angiotensinogen (AGT) and ACE have received the most attention with regard to blood pressure regulation and hypertension. Several lines of evidence suggest that the AGT gene is involved in the pathogenesis of hypertension whereas the results of the studies on the ACE gene polymorphism and hypertension have been mainly negative. In the HERITAGE Family Study cohort, we investigated the associations between the AGT M235T and the ACE I/D polymorphisms and the training responses of blood pressure measured during submaximal (50 Watts) and maximal exercise tests (RANKINEN et al., 1999b). In addition, the possible interactions between the AGT and ACE genotypes for blood pressure training responses were tested.

In Caucasian men (n = 225), the MM homozygotes and the MT heterozygotes of the AGT M235T marker showed decreases of 3.7 (SEM 0.6) and 3.2 (SEM 0.5) mmHg in the submaximal exercise diastolic blood pressure (DBP50) whereas the training response in the TT homozygotes was minimal (−0.4 (SEM 1.0) mmHg) (p for trend 0.016, adjusted for age, body mass index and pre-training DBP50). An association with a borderline significance level (p = 0.050) was observed between the ACE I/D genotype and the DBP50 training response. Men homozygous for the ACE D allele showed greater decreases in DBP50 (4.4 (SEM 0.6) mmHg) than the I/I and I/D genotypes (2.8 (SEM 0.7) and 2.4 (SEM 0.5) mmHg, respectively). A significant (p = 0.022) interaction effect between the AGT and ACE genotypes was observed for the DBP50 training response. Men with the AGT MM and MT genotypes showed decreases in DBP50 regardless of their ACE genotype whereas the AGT TT homozygotes carrying also the ACE D allele showed no response to training. In the sedentary state, i.e. before the endurance training period, the AGT TT homozygotes showed a significantly greater DBP response to acute maximal exercise than the other genotypes. However, the DBP reactivity of the TT homozygotes was alleviated by the endurance training program. In women, the training responses of DBP50 and DBPmax were not associated with the AGT or ACE genotypes. Thus, these HERITAGE Family Study data suggest that, in normotensive sedentary Caucasian men, the genetic variation in the AGT locus modifies the responsiveness of exercise DBP to endurance training, and that interactions between the AGT and ACE loci can alter this response.

Skeletal muscle-specific creatine kinase (CKMM)

The skeletal muscle-specific creatine kinase (CKMM) is an enzyme involved in skeletal muscle energy metabolism by catalyzing the formation of ATP from phosphocreatine (PCr) and ADP. CKMM is more abundant in type II than type I fibers and low CKMM levels are typically observed in the skeletal muscles of endurance athletes.

In a CKMM knock-out mice, the initial isometric maximal twitch force and the twitch time to peak tension were similar to those observed in their wild-type controls (VAN DEURSEN et al., 1993). However, the muscle force of the mutant animals induced by continuous electrical stimulation (1 Hz and 5 Hz) showed a rapid drop at the onset of the stimulation but was regained as the stimulation continued and after 225 s was greater than in the wild-type animals, suggesting that the muscles of the mice lacking CKMM were more resistant to fatigue (VAN DEURSEN et al., 1993). The differences between the mutant and wild-type animals were not related to the concentration of the high-energy phosphate compounds in the muscles, since the levels of ATP, PCr, and inorganic phosphate were similar in both animals. Also the hydrolyzation of PCr during exercise (electrical stimulation) was normal in the mutant animals, and the general morphology of the skeletal muscles as well as the size and the distribution of the fiber types were similar in both animals. The most marked differences in the skeletal muscles between the mutant and the wild-type animals were related to the characteristics of the type II fibers. The intermyofibrillar mitochondrial compartment extended over the entire length of the type II fibers in the mutant mice and the mitochondria were larger and more frequently packed in rows than in the wild-type animals. Also the activities of the mitochondrial enzymes involved in the Krebs cycle or the respiratory chain, as well as the glycogen content of the type II fibers, were 50% to 80% greater in CKMM deficient animals.

The association between CKMM polymorphisms and fitness-related phenotypes has been investigated in three studies. An early study indicated that a CKMM protein charge variant was weakly associated with the ability to perform a 90-min endurance test (BOUCHARD et al., 1989b). More recently, both sib-pair linkage and association analyses supported the hypothesis of a role of the CKMM gene locus in the regulation of the VO_2max response to a 20-week supervised endurance training program in the Caucasian subjects of the HERITAGE Family Study cohort (RIVERA et al., 1997a, RIVERA et al., 1999). In the sedentary state, the parents who were homozygotes for the rare allele of the CKMM Ncol marker had a lower VO_2max than the other two genotypes (RIVERA et al., 1997a). Moreover, both in parents and in offspring, the same genotype was associatied with a lower VO_2max training

response. However, in the GENEATHLETE cohort, both the allele and the genotype frequencies were similar in endurance athletes and in sedentary controls (RIVERA et al., 1997b). This may indicate that the variation in the CKMM gene locus modifies the trainability of VO_2max in sedentary subjects but is not a key determinant of the elite endurance athlete status.

5. Conclusions

The data reviewed in this chapter indicates that several physical activity and cardiorespiratory fitness related traits are influenced by genetic factors with total heritability estimates ranging from 20% to 50%. The majority of the evidence available to date is derived from genetic epidemiology studies but data based on molecular studies have started to emerge recently. Since these traits are multifactorial and the genetic effects seem to be polygenic, the identification of the DNA sequence variation underlying these genetic effects will be a difficult undertaking. However, by using a wide range of designs and techniques, such as case-control and association studies, family studies, linkage studies from genomic scans or with candidate genes, transmission disequilibrium tests, differential display methods and various animal models (transgenic, crossbreeding, gene targeting), the genetic dissection of physical activity and cardiorespiratory fitness phenotypes will be possible. Once available, these data, together with the results from basic and applied research at the phenotypic level, will help to understand not only the pathological processes leading to the chronic diseases associated with a sedentary mode of life, but also the exact mechanisms by which regular physical activity exerts its beneficial health effects. Ultimately, this should lead to more efficient use of physical activity in the primary and secondary prevention of chronic diseases.

References:

AARNIO, M.; WINTER, T.; KUJALA, U. M.; KAPRIO, J. (1997): Familial Aggregation of leisure-time physical activity – a three generation study. In: *International Journal of Sports Medicine, 18*, 549–556.

ADAMS, T. D.; YANOWITZ, F. G.; FISHER, G.; RIDGES, J. D.; NELSON, A. G.; HAGAN, A. D.; WILLIAMS, R. R.; HUNT, S. C. (1986): Genetics and cardiac size. In: MALINA, R. M.; BOUCHARD, C. (eds.): *Sport and human genetics.* Champaign, IL.: Human Kinetics, 131–145.

ARCASOY, M. O.; DEGAR, B. A.; HARRIS, K. W.; FORGET, B. G. (1997): Familial erythrocytosis associated with a short deletion in the erythropoietin receptor gene. In: *Blood, 89*, 4628–4635.

ARDEN, N. K.; SPECTOR, T. D. (1997): Genetic influences on muscle strength, lean body mass, and bone mineral density: a twin study. In: *Journal of Bone and Mineral Research, 12*, 2076–2081.

BERK, M.; DESAI, S. Y.; HEYMAN, H. C.; COLMENARES, C. (1997): Mice lacking the ski proto-oncogene have defects in neurulation, craniofacial patterning, and skeletal muscle development. In: *Genes and Development, 11*, 2029–2039.

BIELEN, E.; FAGARD, R.; AMERY, A. (1991a): The inheritance of left ventricular structure and function assessed by imaging and Doppler echocardiography. In: *American Heart Journal, 121*, 1743–1749.

BIELEN, E. C.; FAGARD, R. H.; AMERY, A. K. (1991b): Inheritance of acute cardiac changes during bicycle exercise: an echocardiographic study in twins. In: *Medicine and Science in Sports and Exercise, 23*, 1254–1259.

BORECKI, I. B.; RICE, T.; BOUCHARD, C.; RAO, D. C. (1991): Commingling analysis of generalized body mass and composition measures: the Québec Family Study. In: *International Journal of Obesity, 15*, 763–773.

BOUCHARD, C. (1983): Human adaptability may have a genetic basis. In: LANDRY, F. (ed.): *Health risk estimation, risk reduction and health promotion.* Canadian Public Health Association.

BOUCHARD, C. (1995): Individual differences in the response to regular exercise. In: *International Journal of Obesity, 19*, 5–8.

BOUCHARD, C.; AN, P.; RICE, T.; SKINNER, J. S.; WILMORE, J. H.; GAGNON, J.; PÉRUSSE, L.; LEON, A. S.; RAO, D. C. (1999): Familial aggregation of VO$_2$max in response to exercise training: results from the HERITAGE Family Study. In: *Journal of Applied Physiology, 87*, 1003–1008.

BOUCHARD, C.; CHAGNON, M.; THIBAULT, M. C.; BOULAY, M. R.; MARCOTTE, M.; COTE, C.; SIMONEAU, J. A. (1989b): Muscle genetic variants and relationship with performance and trainability. In: *Medicine and Science in Sports and Exercise, 21*, 71–77.

BOUCHARD, C.; CHAGNON, M.; THIBAULT, M. C.; BOULAY, M. R.; MARCOTTE, M.; SIMONEAU, J. A. (1988b): Absence of charge variants in human skeletal muscle enzymes of the glycolytic pathway. In: *Human Genetics, 78*, 100.

BOUCHARD, C.; DAW, E. W.; RICE, T.; PÉRUSSE, L.; GAGNON, J.; PROVINCE, M. A.; LEON, A. S.; RAO, D. C.; SKINNER, J. S.; WILMORE, J. H. (1998): Familial resemblance for VO$_2$max in the sedentary state: The HERITAGE Family Study. In: *Medicine and Science in Sports and Exercise, 30*, 252–258.

BOUCHARD, C.; DIONNE, F. T.; SIMONEAU, J. A.; BOULAY, M. R. (1992): Genetics of aerobic and anaerobic performances. In: *Exercise and Sport Sciences Reviews, 20*, 27–58.

BOUCHARD, C.; LEON, A. S.; RAO, D. C.; SKINNER, J. S.; WILMORE, J. H.; GAGNON, J.

(1995): The HERITAGE Family Study: aims, design, and measurement protocol. In: *Medicine and Science in Sports and Exercise, 27,* 721–729.

BOUCHARD, C.; LESAGE, R.; LORTIE, G.; SIMONEAU, J.-A.; HAMEL, P.; BOULAY, M. R.; PERUSSE, L.; THERIAULT, G. (1986a): Aerobic performance in brothers, dizygotic and monozygotic twins. In: *Medicine and Science in Sports and Exercise, 18,* 639–646.

BOUCHARD, C.; PÉRUSSE, L.; LEBLANC, C.; TREMBLAY, A.; THÉRIAULT, G. (1988a): Inheritance of the amount and distribution of human body fat. In: *International Journal of Obesity, 12,* 205–215.

BOUCHARD, C.; SHEPHARD, R. J.; STEPHENS, T. (1994a): *Physical Activity, Fitness, and Health.* International Proceedings and Consensus Statement. Champaign, IL: Human Kinetics.

BOUCHARD, C.; SIMONEAU, J. A.; LORTIE, G.; BOULAY, M. R.; MARCOTTE, M.; THIBAULT, M. C. (1986b): Genetic effects in human skeletal muscle fiber type distribution and enzyme activities. In: *Canadian Journal of Physiology and Pharmacology, 64,* 1245–1251.

BOUCHARD, C.; TREMBLAY, A.; DESPRÉS, J. P.; NADEAU, A.; LUPIEN, P. J.; THÉRIAULT, G.; DUSSAULT, J.; MOORJANI, S.; PINEAULT, S.; FOURNIER, G. (1990): The response to long-term overfeeding in identical twins. In: *New England Journal of Medicine, 322,* 1477–1482.

BOUCHARD, C.; TREMBLAY, A.; DESPRÉS, J. P.; THÉRIAULT, G.; NADEAU, A.; LUPIEN, P. J.; MOORJANI, S.; PRUD'HOMME, D.; FOURNIER, G. (1994b): The response to exercise with constant energy intake in identical twins. In: *Obesity Research, 2,* 400–410.

BOUCHARD, C.; TREMBLAY, A.; NADEAU, A.; DESPRÉS, J. P.; THÉRIAULT, G.; BOULAY, M. R.; LORTIE, G.; LEBLANC, C.; FOURNIER, G. (1989a): Genetic effect in resting and exercise metabolic rates. In: *Metabolism, 38,* 364–370.

VAN DEN BREE, M. B.; SCHIEKEN, R. M.; MOSKOWITZ, W. B.; EAVES, L. J. (1996): Genetic Regulation of Hemodynamic Variables During Dynamic Exercise. The MCV Twin Study. In: *Circulation, 94,* 1864–1869.

CHENG, L. S. C.; CARMELLI, D.; HUNT, S. C.; WILLIAMS, R. R. (1997): Segregation analysis of Cardiovascular reactivity to laboratory Stressors. In: *Genetic Epidemiology, 14,* 35–49.

CLAYTON, D. A. (1982): Replication of animal mitochondrial DNA. In: *Cell, 28,* 693–705.

COOK, E. H. JR; STEIN, M. A.; KRASOWSKI, M. D.; COX, N. J.; OLKON, D. M.; KIEFFER, J. E.; LEVENTHAL, B. L. (1995): Association of attention-deficit disorder and the dopamine transporter gene. In: *American Journal of Human Genetics, 56,* 933–998.

CUNEO, R. C.; SALOMON, F.; WILES, C. M.; HESP, R.; SONKSEN, P. H. (1991): Growth hormone treatment in growth hormone-deficient adults. I. Effects on muscle mass and strength. In: *Journal of Applied Physiology, 70,* 688–694.

DE LA CHAPELLE, A.; TRASKELIN, A.-L.; JUVONEN, E. (1993): Truncated erythropoietin receptor causes dominantly inherited benign human erythrocytosis. In: *Proceedings of the National Academy of Sciences USA, 90,* 4495–4499.

VAN DEURSEN, J; HEERSCHAP, A.; OERLEMANS, F.; RUITENBEEK, W.; JAP, P.; TER LAAK, H.; WIERINGA, B. (1993): Skeletal muscles of mice deficient in muscle creatine kinase lack burst activity. In: *Cell, 74,* 621–631.

DEYSSIG, R.; FRISCH, H.; BLUM, W. F.; WALDHOR, T. (1993): Effect of growth hormone treatment on hormonal parameters, body composition and strength in athletes. In: *Acta Endocrinologica, 128,* 313–318.

DIONNE, F. T.; TURCOTTE, L.; THIBAULT, M. C.; BOULAY, M. R.; SKINNER, J. S.; BOUCHARD, C. (1991): Mitochondrial DNA sequence polymorphism, VO_2 max and response to endurance training. In: *Medicine and Science in Sports and Exercise, 23,* 177–185.

FAGARD, R.; BIELEN, E.; AMERY, A. (1991): Heritability fo aerobic power and anaerobic energy generation during exercise. In: *Journal of Applied Physiology, 70,* 357–362.

GAGNON, J.; HO-KIM, M. A.; CHAGNON, Y. C.; PÉRUSSE, L.; DIONNE, F. T.; LEON, A. S.; RAO, D. C.; SKINNER, J. S.; WILMORE, J. H.; BOUCHARD, C. (1997): Absence of linkage between VO_2max and its response to training with markers spanning chromosome 22. In: *Medicine and Science in Sports and Exercise, 29,* 1448–1453.

GAINETDINOV, R. R.; WETSEL, W. C.; JONES, S. R.; LEVIN, E. D.; JABER, M.; CARON, M. G. (1999): Role of serotonin in the paradoxical effect of psychostimulants on hyperactivity. In: *Science, 283,* 397–401.

GAYAGAY, G.; YU, B.; HAMBLY, B.; BOSTON, T.; HAHN, A.; CELERMAJER, D. S.; TRENT, R. J. (1998): Elite endurance athletes and the ACE I allele - the role of genes in athletic performance. In: *Human Genetics, 103,* 48–50.

GIBBONS, L. E.; VIDEMAN, T.; BATTIÉ, M. C.; KAPRIO, J. (1998): Determinants of paraspinal mucle cross-sectional area in male monozygotic twins. In: *Physical Therapy, 78,* 602–610.

GILL, M.; DALY, G.; HERON, S.; HAWI, Z.; FITZGERALD, M. (1997): Confirmation of association between attention deficit hyperactivity disorder and a dopamine transporter polymorphism. In: *Mol Psychiatry, 2,* 311–313.

GREENBERG, B. D.; NEWBOLD, J. E.; SUGINO, A. (1983): Intraspecific nucleotide sequence variability surrounding the origin of replication in human mitochondrial DNA. In: *Gene, 21,* 33–49.

GROBET, L.; ROYO MARTIN, L. J.; PONCELET, D.; PIROTTIN, D.; BROUWERS, B.; RIQUET, J.; SCHOEBERLEIN, A.; DUNNER, S.; MÉNISSIER, F.; MASSABANDA, J.; FRIES, R.; HANSET, R.; GEORGES, M. (1997): A deletion in the bovine myostatin gene causes the double-muscled phenotype in cattle. In: *Nature Genetics, 17,* 71–74.

HAGBERG, J. M.; FERRELL, R. E.; McCOLE, S. D.; WILUND, K. R.; MOORE, G. E. (1998): VO_2max is associated with ACE genotype in postmenopausal women. In: *Journal of Applied Physiology, 85,* 1842–1846.

HAMEL, P.; SIMONEAU, J.-A.; LORTIE, G.; BOULAY, M. R.; BOUCHARD, C. (1986): Heredity and muscle adaptation to endurance training. In: *Medicine and Science in Sports and Exercise, 18,* 690–696.

HAMET, P.; PAUSOVA, Z.; ADARICHEV, V.; ADARICHEVA, K.; TREMBLAY, J. (1998): Hypertension: genes and environment. In: *Journal of Hypertension, 16,* 397–418.

HELLER, R. F.; O'CONNEL, D. L.; ROBERTS, D. C. K.; ALLEN, J. R.; KNAPP, J. C.; STEELE, P. L.; SILOVE, D. (1988): Lifestyle factors in monozygotic and dizygotic twins. In: *Genetic Epidemiology, 5,* 311–321.

HOWALD, H. (1976): Ultrastructure and biochemical function of skeletal muscle in twins. In: *Annals of Human Biology, 3,* 455–462.

JANSSEN, Y. J.; DOORNBOS, J.; ROELFSEMA, F. (1999): Changes in muscle volume, strength, and bioenergetics during recombinant human growth hormone (GH) therapy in adults with GH deficiency. In: *Journal of Clinical Endocrinology and Metabolism, 84,* 279–284.

JUVONEN, E.; IKKALA, E.; FYHRQUIST, F.; RUUTU, T. (1991): Autosomal dominant erythrocytosis caused by increased sensitivity to erythropoietin. In: *Blood, 78,* 3066–3069.

KAPRIO, J.; KOSKENVUO, M.; SARNA, S. (1981): Cigarette smoking, use of alcohol, and leisure-time physical activity among same-sexed adult male twins. In: *Progress in clinical and biological research.* New York: Alan R. Liss, 37–46.

KELLY, M. A.; RUBINSTEIN, M.; PHILLIPS, T. J.; LESSOV, C. N.; BURKHART-KASCH, S.; ZHANG, G.; BUNZOW, J. R.; FANG, Y.; GERHARDT, G. A.; GRANDY, D. K.; LOW, M. J. (1998): Locomotor activity in D2 dopamine receptor-deficient mice is determined by gene dosage, genetic background, and developmental adaptations. In: *Journal of Neuroscience, 18,* 3470–3479.

KOMI, P. V.; VIITASALO, J. H. T.; HAVU, M.; THROSTENSSON, A.; SJODIN, B.; KARISSON, J.

(1977): Skeletal muscle fibres and muscle enzyme activities in monozygotous and dizygous twins of both sexes. In: *Acta Physiologica Scandinavica, 100,* 385–392.

KOOPMANS, J. R.; VAN DOORNEN, L. J. P.; BOOMSMA, D. I. (1994): Smoking and sports participation. In: Godlbourt, U.; De Faire, U.; Berg, K. (eds.): *Genetic factors in coronary heart disease.* Lancaster, UK: Kluwer Academic, 217-235.

KRALOVICS, R.; INDRAK, K.; STOPKA, T.; BERMAN, B. W.; PRCHAL, J. F.; PRCHAL, J. T. (1997): Two new EPO receptor mutations: truncated EPO reveptors are most frequently associated with primary familial and congenital polycythemias. In: *Blood, 90,* 2057–2061.

LANDRY, F.; BOUCHARD, C.; DUMESNIL, J. (1985): Cardiac dimension changes with endurance training. In: *JAMA, 254,* 77–80.

LAUDERDALE, D. S.; FABSITZ, R.; MEYER, J. M.; SHOLINSKY, P.; RAMAKRISHNAN, V.; GOLDBERG, J. (1997): Familial determinants of moderate and intense physical activity: a twin study. In: *Medicine and Science in Sports and Exercise, 29,* 1062–1068.

LAUWERYNS, I.; CARELS, C.; MARCHAL, G.; BELLON, E.; HERMANS, R.; VLIETINCK, R. (1995): Magnetic resonance imaging of the masseter muscle: a preliminary genetic study in monozygotic and dizygotic twins. In: *Journal of Craniofacial Genetics and Developmental Biology, 15,* 26–34.

LESAGE, R.; SIMONEAU, J. A.; JOBIN, J.; LEBLANC, J.; BOUCHARD, C. (1985): Familial resemblance in maximal heart rate, blood lactate and aerobic power. In: *Human Heredity, 35,* 182–189.

LONGMORE, G. D. (1993): Erythropoietin receptor mutations and Olympic glory. In: *Nature Genetics, 4,* 108–110.

LORTIE, G.; SIMONEAU, J. A.; HAMEL, P.; BOULAY, M. R.; LANDRY, F.; BOUCHARD, C. (1984): Responses of maximal aerobic power and capacity to aerobic training. In: *International Journal of Sports Medicine, 5,* 232–236.

MAES, H. H.; BEUNEN, G. P.; VLIETINCK, R. F.; NEALE, M. C.; THOMIS, M.; VANDEN EYNDE, B.; LYSENS, R.; SIMONS, J.; DEROM, C.; DEROM (1996): Inheritance of physical fitness in 10-yr-old twins and their parents. In: *Medicine and Science in Sports and Exercise, 28,* 1479–1491.

MARCOTTE, M.; CHAGNON, M.; CÔTÉ, C.; THIBAULT, M. C.; BOULAY, M. R.; BOUCHARD, C. (1987): Lack of genetic polymorphism in human skeletal muscles enzymes of the tricarboxylic acid cycle. In: *Human Genetics, 77,* 200.

McGUE, M.; HIRSCH, B.; LYKKEN, D. T. (1993): Age and the self-perception of ability: A twin study analysis. In: *Psychology and Aging, 8,* 72–80.

McGUIRE, S.; NEIDERHISER, J. M.; REISS, E.; HETHERINGTON, E. M.; PLOMIN, R. (1994): Genetic and environmental influences on perceptions of self-worth and competence in adolescence: a study of twins, full siblings, and step-siblings. In: *Child Development, 65,* 785–799.

McPHERRON, A. C.; LAWLER, A. M.; LEE, S.-J. (1997): Regulation of skeletal muscle mass in mice by a new TGFâ superfamily member. In: Nature, 378, 83-90.

McPHERRON, A. C.; LEE, S.-J. (1997): Double muscling in cattle due to mutations in the myostatin gene. In: *Proceedings of the National Academy of Sciences USA, 94,* 12457–12461.

MONTGOMERY, H.; CLARKSON, P.; BARNARD, M.; BELL, J.; BRYNES, A.; DOLLERY, C.; HAJNAL, J.; HEMINGWAY, H.; MERCER, D.; JARMAN, P.; MARSHALL, R.; PRASAD, K.; RAYSON, M.; SAEED, N.; TALMUD, P.; THOMAS L.; JUBB, M.; WORLD, M.; HUMPHRIES, S. (1999): Angiotensin-converting enzyme gene insertion/deletion polymorphism and response to physical training. In: *Lancet, 353,* 541–545.

MONTGOMERY, H.; CLARKSON, P.; DOLLERY, C. M.; PRASAD, K.; LOSI, M.-A.; HEMINGWAY, H.; STATTERS, D.; JUBB, M.; GIRVAIN, M.; VARNAVA, A.; WORLD, M.; DEANFIELD, J.; TALMUD, P.; McEWAN, J. R.; McKENNA, W. J.; HUMPHRIES, S. (1997): Association of angiotensin-converting enzyme gene I/D polymorphism with change in left ventricular mass in response to physical training. In: *Circulation, 96,* 741–747.

MONTGOMERY, H. E.; MARSHALL, R.; HEMINGWAY, H.; MYERSON, S.; CLARKSON, P.; DOLLERY, C.; HAYWARD, M.; HOLLIMAN, D. E.; JUBB, M.; WORLD, M., THOMAS, E. L.; BRYNES, A. E.; SAEED, N.; BARNARD, M.; BELL, J. D.; PRASAD, K.; RAYSON, M.; TALMUD, P. J.; HUMPHRIES, S. E. (1998): Human gene for physical performance. In: *Nature, 393,* 221–222.

MOORE, L. L.; LOMBARDI, D. A.; WHITE, M. J.; CAMPBELL, J. L.; OLIVERIA, S. A.; ELLISON, S. A. (1991): Influence of parents' physical activity levels of young children. In: *Journal of Pediatrics, 118,* 215–219.

NAKAMURA, T.; MASUI, S.; WADA, M.; KATOH, H.; MIKAMI, H.; KATSUTA, S. (1993): Heredity of muscle fibre composition estimated from a selection experiment in rats. In: *European Journal of Applied Physiology, 66,* 85–89.

NIMMO, M. A.; WILSON, R. H.; SNOW, D. H. (1985): The inheritance of skeletal muscle fibre composition in mice. In: *Comparative Biochemistry and Physiology, 81A,* 109–115.

NGUYEN, T. V.; HOWARD, G. M.; KELLY, P. J.; EISMAN, J. A. (1998): Bone mass, lean mass and fat mass: same genes of same environments? In: *American Journal of Epidemiology, 147,* 3-16.

NORMAN, B.; MAHNKE-ZIZELMAN, K.; VALLIS, A.; SABINA, R. L. (1998a): Genetic and other determinants of AMP deaminase activity in healthy adult skeletal muscle. In: *Journal of Applied Physiology, 85,* 1273–1278.

NORMAN, B.; SABINA, R. L.; ESBJÖRNSSON-LILJEDAHL, M.; JANSSON, E. (1998b): ATP metabolism during sprint exercise in subjects with different genotype for AMP deaminase in skeletal muscle. In: *Journal of Physiology, 506,* 117.

OSBORNE, K. A.; ROBICHON, A.; BURGESS, E.; BUTLAND, S.; SHAW, R. A.; COULTHARD, A.; PEREIRA, H. S.; GREENSPAN, R. J.; SOKOLO-

WSKI, M. B. (1997): Natural behaviour polymorphism due to a cGMP-dependent protein kinase of Drosophila. In: *Science, 277,* 834–836.

PALMITER, R. D.; BRINSTER, R. L.; HAMMER, R. E.; TRUMBAUER, M. E.; ROSENFELD, M. G.; BIRNBERG, N. C.; EVANS, R. M. (1982): Dramatic growth of mice that develop from eggs microinjected with metallothionein-growth hormone fusion genes. In: *Nature, 300,* 611–615.

PALMITER, R. D.; NORSTEDT, G.; GELINAS, R. E.; HAMMER, R. E.; BRINSTER, R. L. (1983): Metallothionein-human GH fusion genes stimulate growth of mice. In: *Science, 222,* 809–814.

PARK, J. H.; BROWN, R. L.; PARK, C. R.; COHN, M.; CHANCE, B. (1988): Energy metabolism of the untrained muscle of elite runners as observed by 31P magnetic resonance spectroscopy: evidence suggesting a genetic endowment for endurance exercise. In: *Proceedings of the National Academy of Sciences USA, 85,* 8780–8784.

PÉRUSSE, L.; LEBLANC, C.; BOUCHARD, C. (1988): Inter-generation transmission of physical fitness in the canadian population. In: *Canadian Journal of Sport Sciences, 13,* 8–14.

PÉRUSSE, L.; LORTIE, G.; LEBLANC, C.; TREMBLAY, A.; THÉRIAULT, G.; BOUCHARD, C. (1987): Genetic and environmental sources of variation in physical fitness. In: *Annals of Human Biology, 14,* 425–434.

PÉRUSSE, L.; TREMBLAY, A.; LEBLANC, C.; BOUCHARD, C. (1989): Genetic and environmental influences on level of habitual physical activity and exercise participation. In: *American Journal of Epidemiology, 129,* 1012–1022.

PICKERING, T. G.; GERIN, W. (1994): Genetic factors, cardiovascular reactivity and blood pressure variability. In: Goldbourt, U.; deFaire, U.; Berg, K. (eds.): *Genetic factors in coronary heart disease.* Dordrecht: Kluwer Academic, 385–396.

PRUD'HOMME, D.; BOUCHARD, C.; LEBLANC, C.; LANDRY, F.; FONTAINE, E. (1984): Sensitivity of maximal aerobic power to training is genotype-dependent. In: *Medicine and Science in Sports and Exercise, 16*, 489–493.

RANKINEN, T.; GAGNON, J.; PÉRUSSE, L.; CHAGNON, Y.; RICE, T.; LEON, A. S.; SKINNER, J. S.; WILMORE, J. H.; RAO, D. C.; BOUCHARD, C. (1999b): *Interaction between angiotensinogen and angiotensin-converting enzyme polymorphisms for exercise blood pressure: The HERITAGE Family Study*. Submitted for publication.

RANKINEN, T.; PÉRUSSE, L.; GAGNON, J.; LEON, A. S.; SKINNER, J.; WILMORE, J.; RAO, D. C.; BOUCHARD, C. (1999a): *Angiotensin-converting enzyme I/D polymorphism and trainability of the fitness phenotypes. The HERITAGE Family Study*. Submitted for publication.

RAVUSSIN, E.; LILLIOJA, S.; KNOWLER, W. C.; CHRISTIN, L.; FREYMOND, D.; ABBOTT, G. H.; BOYCE, V.; HOWARD, B. V.; BOGARDUS, C. (1988): Reduced rate of energy expenditure as a risk factor for body weight gain. In: *New England Journal of Medicine, 318*, 467–472.

RICE, T.; BORECKI, I. B.; BOUCHARD, C.; RAO, D. C. (1993): Segregation analysis of fat mass and other body composition measures derived from underwater weighing. In: *American Journal of Human Genetics, 52*, 967–973.

RIVERA, M. A.; DIONNE, F. T.; SIMONEAU, J. A.; PÉRUSSE, L.; CHAGNON, M.; CHAGNON, Y. C.; GAGNON, J.; LEON, A. S.; RAO, D. C.; SKINNER, J. S.; WILMORE, J. H.; BOUCHARD, C. (1997a): Muscle-specific creatine kinase gene polymorphism and VO$_2$max in the HERITAGE Family Study. In: *Medicine and Science in Sports and Exercise, 29*, 1311–1317.

RIVERA, M. A.; DIONNE, F. T.; WOLFARTH, B.; CHAGNON, M.; SIMONEAU, J. A.; PÉRUSSE, L.; BOULAY, M. R.; GAGNON, J.; SONG, T. M. K.; KEUL, J.; BOUCHARD, C. (1997b): Muscle-specific creatine kinase gene polymorphisms in elite endurance athletes and sedentary controls. In: *Medicine and Science in Sports and Exercise, 29*, 1444–1447.

RIVERA, M. A.; PÉRUSSE, L.; SIMONEAU, J. A.; GAGNON, J.; DIONNE, F. T.; LEON, A. S.; SKINNER, J. S.; WILMORE, J. H.; PROVINCE, M.; RAO, D. C.; BOUCHARD, C. (1999): Linkage between a muscle-specific CK gene marker and VO$_2$max in the HERITAGE Family Study. In: *Medicine and Science in Sports and Exercise, 31(5)*, 698–701.

RIVERA, M. A.; WOLFARTH, B.; DIONNE, F. T.; CHAGNON, M.; SIMONEAU, J. A.; BOULAY, M. R.; SONG, T. M. K.; PÉRUSSE, L.; GAGNON, J.; LEON, A. S.; RAO, D. C.; SKINNER, J. S.; WILMORE, J. H.; KEUL, J.; BOUCHARD, C. (1998): Three mitochondrial DNA restriction polymorphisms in elite endurance athletes and sedentary controls. In: *Medicine and Science in Sports and Exercise, 30*, 687–690.

SEEMAN, E.; HOPPER, J. L.; YOUNG, N. R.; FORMICA, C.; GOSS, P.; TSALAMANDRIS, C. (1996): Do genetic factors explain associations between muscle strength, lean mass, and bone density? A twin study. In: *American Journal of Physiology, 270*, 320–327.

SIMONEAU, J. A.; BOUCHARD, C. (1995): Genetic determinism of fiber type proportion in human skeletal muscle. In: *FASEB Journal, 9*, 1091–1095.

SIMONEAU, J. A.; LORTIE, G.; BOULAY, M. R.; MARCOTTE, M.; THIBAULT, M.-C.; BOUCHARD, C. (1986): Inheritance of human skeletal muscle and anaerobic capacity adaptation to high-intensity intermittent training. In: *International Journal of Sports Medicine, 7*, 167–171.

SOKOL, L.; LUHOVY, M.; GUAN, Y.; PRCHAL, J. F.; SEMENZA, G. L.; PRCHAL, J. T. (1995): Primary familial polycythemia: a frameshift mutation in the erythropoietin receptor gene and increased sensitivity of erythroid progenitors to erythropoietin. In: *Blood, 86*, 15–22.

SUNDET, J. M.; MAGNUS, P.; TAMBS, K. (1994): The heritability of maximal aerobic power: a study of Norwegian twins. In: *Scandinavian Journal of Medicine and Science in Sports, 4*, 181–185.

Sutrave, P.; Kelly, A. M.; Hughes, S. H. (1990): ski can cause selective growth of skeletal muscle in transgenic mice. In: *Genes and Development, 4,* 1462–1472.

Taaffe, D. R.; Jin, I. H.; Vu, T. H.; Hoffman, A. R.; Marcus, R. (1996): Lack of effect of recombinant human growth hormone (GH) on muscle morphology and GH-insulin-like growth factor expression in resistance-trained elderly men. In: *Journal of Clinical Endocrinology and Metabolism, 81,* 421–425.

Taaffe, D. R.; Pruitt, L.; Reim, J.; Hintz, R. L.; Butterfield, G.; Hoffman, A. R.; Marcus, R. (1994): Effect of recombinant human growth hormone on the muscle strength response to resistance exercise in elderly men. In: *Journal of Clinical Endocrinology and Metabolism, 79,* 1361–1366.

Thériault, G.; Diano, R.; Leblanc, C.; Pérusse, L.; Landry, F.; Bouchard, C. (1986): The role of heredity in cardiac size: an echocardiographic study on twins, brothers and sisters, and sibs by adoption. In: *Medicine and Science in Sports and Exercise, 18,* 51.

Thibault, M. C.; Simoneau, J. A.; Côté, C.; Boulay, M. R.; Lagassé, P.; Marcotte, M.; Bouchard, C. (1986): Inheritance of human muscle enzyme adaptation to isokinetic strength training. In: *Human Heredity, 36,* 341–347.

Thomis, M. A.; Van Leemputte, M.; Maes, H. H.; Blimkie, C. J. R.; Claessens, A. L.; Marchal, G.; Willems, E.; Vlietinck, R. F.; Beunen, G. P. (1997): Multivariate genetic analysis of maximal isometric muscle force at different elbow angles. In: *Journal of Applied Physiology, 82,* 959–967.

Toubro, S.; Sørensen, T. I. A.; Rønn, B.; Christensen, N. J.; Astrup, A. (1996): Twenty-four-hour energy expenditure: the role of body composition, thyroid status, sympathetic activity, and family membership. In: *Journal of Clinical Endocrinology and Metabolism, 81,* 2670–2674.

Verhaaren, H. A.; Schieken, R. M.; Mosteller, M.; Hewitt, J. K.; Eaves, L. J.; Nance, W. E. (1991): Bivariate genetic analysis of left ventricular mass and weight in pubertal twins (The Medical College of Virginia Twin Study). In: *American Journal of Cardiology, 68,* 661–668.

Waldman, I. D.; Rowe, D. C.; Abramowitz, A.; Kozel, S. T.; Mohr, J. H.; Sherman, S. L.; Cleveland, H. H.; Sanders, M. L.; Gard, J. M.; Stever, C. (1998): Association and linkage of the dopamine transporter gene and attention-deficit hyperactivity disorder in children: heterogeneity owing to diagnostic subtype and severity. In: *American Journal of Human Genetics, 63,* 1767–1776.

Wolf, E.; Wanke, R.; Schenck, E.; Hermanns, E.; Brem, G. (1995): Effects of growth hormone overproduction on grip strength of transgenic mice. In: *European Journal of Endocrinology, 133,* 735–740.

Yarasheski, K. E.; Campbell, J. A.; Smith, K.; Rennie, M. J.; Holloszy, J. O.; Bier, D. M. (1992): Effect of growth hormone and resistance exercise on muscle growth in young men. In: *American Journal of Physiology, 262,* 261–267.

Yarasheski, K. E.; Zachwieja, J. J.; Angelopoulos, T. J.; Bier, D. M. (1993): Short-term growth hormone treatment does not increase muscle protein synthesis in experienced weight lifters. In: *Journal of Applied Physiology, 74,* 3073–3076.

Yarasheski, K. E.; Zachwieja, J. J.; Campbell, J. A.; Bier, D. M. (1995): Effect of growth hormone and resistance exercise on muscle growth and strength in older men. In: *American Journal of Physiology, 268,* 268–276.

Zachwieja, J. J.; Toffolo, G.; Cobelli, C.; Bier, D. M.; Yarasheski, K. E. (1996): Resistance exercise and growth hormone adminsistration in older men: effects on insulin sensitivity and secretion during a stable-label intravenous glucose tolerance test. In: *Metabolism, 45,* 254–260.

Bente Klarlund Pedersen

Physical Activity and the Immune System – for the Better and the Worse

The Copenhagen Muscle Research Centre, Department of Infectious Diseases, Rigshospitalet, University of Copenhagen, Denmark

1. Introduction

Many individuals claim that regular exercise increases resistance to infections such as the common cold (FITZGERALD, 1988; NASH, 1987). On the other hand, there have also been anecdotal reports from athletes and their coaches that hard training is associated with increased respiratory tract infections (FITZGERALD,

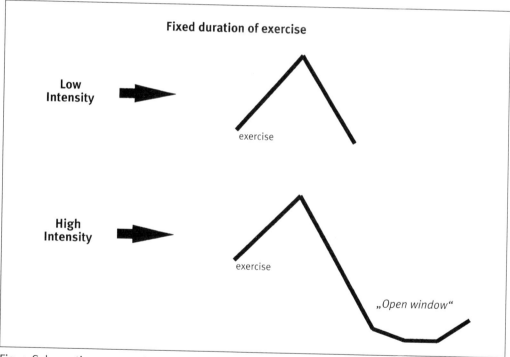

Fixed duration of exercise

Low Intensity

exercise

High Intensity

exercise

„Open window"

Fig. 1. Schematic presentation of the effects of exercise at low and high intensity with fixed duration of time. In the model are included the exercise-effects on lymphocyte number, natural killer and lymphokine activated killer cell activities and antibody production. During intense and high intensity exercise, the immune system is enhanced, but intense exercise is followed by a period of immunosuppression during which there is an „Open window" of opportunity for pathogens.

1988). Today epidemiological evidence exists which supports the anecdotal impression (NIEMAN; HENSON, 1994), and it has become clear that the function of the immune system is enhanced by moderate physical activity and may be somewhat responsible for exercise-related reduction in illness. In contrast, it has been repeatedly shown that intense exercise causes inhibition of the function of the immune system in the recovery phase following intense exercise (HOFFMAN-GOETZ; PEDERSEN, 2000). This chapter provides an overview of the effects of acute and chronic exercise on the immune system and discusses the clinical significance of these findings.

2. Acute exercise and the cellular immune system

2.1 Leukocyte subpopulations

In response to acute exercise, lymphocytes are mobilized to blood. Thus the lymphocyte concentration is increased when measured during or immediately after the exercise. However, following strenuous exercise the lymphocyte count decreases below prevalue (MCCARTHY; DALE, 1988). The increased lymphocyte concentration is due to recruitment of all lymphocyte subpopulations to the blood. Thus, both CD4+ T cells, CD8+ T cells, CD19+ B cells, CD16+ natural killer (NK) cells, and CD56+ NK cells increase during exercise. Simultaneously, the CD4/CD8 ratio decreases, because the CD8 count increases more than the CD4 count. The percentage of CD4+ cells declines primarily due to the fact that NK cells increase more than any other lymphocyte subpopulation. Accordingly, the relative fraction of lymphocyte subpopulations changes.

2.2 NK cell activity

NK cells mediate non-major histocompatibility complex (MHC)-restricted cytotoxicity and offer potential resistance to viral infections (WELSH; VARGAS-CORTES, 1992). They also mediate cytotoxic activity against some malignant cells (O'SHEA; ORTALDO, 1992). The cytotoxic activity of NK cells is enhanced by interferon (IFN)-a (ORTALDO et al., 1983b) and interleukin (IL)-2 (ORTALDO et al., 1983a), whereas certain prostaglandins (BRUNDA et al., 1980) and immune complexes (PEDERSEN et al., 1986) down-regulate the function of NK cells. The in vitro-generated lymphokine activated killer (LAK) cells show a broader range of non-major histocompatibilty (MHC)-restricted target cell killing (GRIMM et al., 1982). NK cells are recruited to the circulation within a few minutes after the onset of exercise and other stressors, and NK cells are more sensitive to stress stimuli than any other subpopulations (PEDERSEN et al., 1994). Results from the era of stress-immunology thus indicate that the rapidly increasing NK cell response in relation to infections probably also includes immediate recruitment of NK cells to the circulation and the site of infection. Since the concentration of NK cells increases more than any other subpopulation of the lymphocytes, this means that the NK cell percentage of blood mononuclear cells (BMNC) increases. Using the in vitro assay measuring the NK cell activity (lysis per fixed number of BMNC) the NK cell lysis increases as a consequence of increased proportion of cells mediating non-MHC-restricted cytotoxicity. During exercise the NK cell activity on a per NK cell basis does not change in some exercise models (NIEMAN et al., 1993b; PALMO et al., 1995), but is reduced in relation to very intense exercise (NIELSEN et al., 1996).

Following intense exercise of long duration, the concentration of NK cells declines below prevalues. Furthermore, the NK and LAK cell activity (lysis per fixed number of BMNC) decreases. The NK cell concentration and the NK cell activity are maximally suppressed 2 to 4 hours after exercise.

The NK cells have been studied in various models, including laboratory and field studies, studies on running, cycling and rowing, studies on concentric, eccentric or combined concentric and eccentric exercise, and exercise lasting from a few minutes to several hours. This has recently been reviewed (PEDERSEN; NIELSEN, 1997).

In general, the NK cell activity is increased when measured immediately after or during both moderate and intense exercise of a few minutes. The intensity, more than the duration of exercise, is responsible for the degree of increment in the number of NK cells. If the exercise has lasted for a long period and has been very intense (e.g. a triathlon race), only a modest increase in NK cells are found post-exercise (ROHDE et al., 1996).

The NK cell count and the NK cell activity is suppressed only following intense exercise of a certain duration, and at least one hour seems to be a critical duration of exercise in terms of post-exercise suppression of natural immunity, Fig. 2. Initial fitness level or sex do not influence the magnitude of exercise-induced changes in NK cells (BRAHMI et al., 1985).

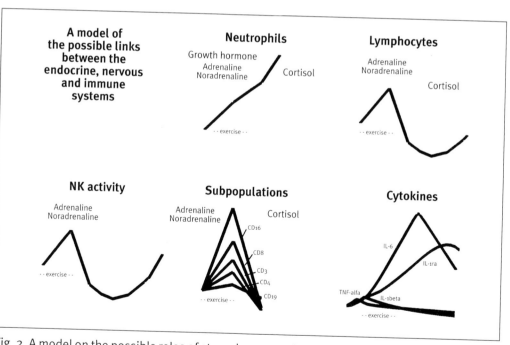

Fig. 2. A model on the possible roles of stress hormones in mediating the acute exercise effects on the immune system.

2.3 Antibody production

The secretory immune system of mucosal tissues such as the upper respiratory tract is considered to be the first barrier to colonization by pathogenic microorganisms causing upper respiratory tract infections (MACKINNON, HOOPER, 1994; BIERMAN et al., 1952; DUFAUX, ORDER, 1989b). IgA is the predominant immunoglobulin class in mucosal secretions, and the level of IgA in mucosal fluids correlates more closely with resistance to upper respiratory tract infections than serum antibodies (LIEW et al., 1984). TOMASI et al. (1982) reported suppressed levels of the salivary IgA in cross-country skiers after a race. This finding was confirmed by a 70% decrease in salivary IgA for several hours after 2 hours of intense ergometer cycling (MACKINNON et al., 1987). Decreased salivary IgA was found after swimming (THARP, BARNES, 1990; GLEESON et al., 1999), in addition salivary IgA was low for several hours after marathon running (MUNS et al., 1989) and incremental treadmill running to exhaustion (McDOWELL et al., 1992). Submaximal exercise of VO_2max had no effect on salivary IgA (HOUSH et al., 1991; McDOWELL et al., 1991). In order to study the mechanism behind the suppression of immunoglobulins a plaque forming cell assay has been used. This assay allows an identification of the individual immunoglobulin-secreting cells of blood. Stimulation of cells with pokeweed mitogen, IL-2 and Epstein-Barr virus resulted in significantly decreased numbers of IgG, IgA and IgM-secreting blood cells during, as well as 2 hours post-exercise. The percentage of B cells among BMNC does not change in relation to exercise, suggesting that the suppression of immunoglobulin-secreting cells is not due to changes in numbers of B cells. Purified B cells produce plaques only after stimulation with Epstein-Barr virus and in these cultures no exercise-induced suppression was found. The addition of indomethacin to IL-2 stimulated cultures of blood mononuclear cells partly reversed the post-exercise suppressed B cell function. Therefore, it was concluded that the exercise-induced suppression of the plaque forming cell response was partly mediated by monocytes (TVEDE et al., 1989).

2.4 Neutrophil function

Neutrophils are considered to be part of the innate immune system, and are essential for host defence. However, they are also involved in the pathology of various inflammatory conditions (SMITH, 1994). One of the more pronounced features of physical activity on immune parameters is the prolonged neutrocytosis following acute long-term exercise (McCARTHY; DALE, 1988). Short bouts of vigorous exercise lasting from approximately 10 seconds to half an hour (e. g. sprinting, rowing or gymnastics), sustained strenuous exercise lasting a few hours (e. g. marathon races), or intermittent vigorous exercise (e. g. American football or soccer), can all induce in the participants an immediate leukocytosis (McCARTHY; DALE, 1988). At the end of short term exercise lasting up to half an hour the leukocyte count usually falls quickly, approaching its normal levels within half an hour. After sustained exercise, lasting 2.5 to 3.5 hours, the leukocyte count returns slowly and is often elevated above preexercise levels at 24 hours. Whereas after intermittent exercise over 1.5 hours or sustained exercise of 1 hour, the leukocyte count continues to rise for 1 to 4 hours, before falling slowly (SMITH et al., 1990; WEIDEMANN et al., 1992; SMITH, 1994).

There are a number of reports showing that exercise triggers a series of changes in the neutrophil population and may affect certain subpopulations differentially. KUROKAWA et al. (1995) reported fall in expression of L-selectin (CD62L) immediately after exercise followed by an increase during recovery, whereas there were no changes in CD11a or CD11b expression. SMITH et al. (1996) showed increased expression of CD11b in response to exercise.

Regarding the function of neutrophils, exercise has both short- and long-term effects. The neutrophil responses to infections include adherence, chemotaxis, phagocytosis, oxidative burst, degranulation and microbial killing. In general, moderate exercise boosts neutrophil functions, including chemotaxis, phagocytosis and the oxidative burst, whereas extreme exercise suppresses these functions with the exception of chemotaxis and degranulation, which are not affected (SMITH et al., 1990; NIEMAN, 1994a; ORTEGA et al., 1993; SMITH et al., 1992; BRINES et al., 1996). In the study by SMITH et al. (1990), neutrophil killing capacity was enhanced for at least 6 hours following 1 hour of moderate ergometer cycle exercise. In another study, immediately following a 20-km race, neutrophils from runners were less able to ingest bacteria, an effect which lasted for 3 days (NIEMAN, 1994b).

In a comparative study of male distance runners, triathletes and untrained controls, progressive exercise to exhaustion doubled neutrophil phagocytic capacity in samples taken up to 24 hours after exercise. Superoxide production in phorbol myristate accetate stimulated cells fell slightly immediately after exercise but then increased one hour later and remained elevated for 24 hours; there were significant changes in chemotactic capacity or random migration (HACK et al., 1992). These results were confirmed by the same group in both trained and untrained individuals (HACK et al., 1994). Phagocytic activity increased immediately after exercise but no changes in adherence or bactericidal activity were described in untrained individuals. However, decreased adherence and bactericidal activity, but no change in phagocytic activity were found in elite cyclists (LEWICKI et al., 1987).

Prolonged impaired neutrophil function has also been reported in race horses following a single strenuous event (BUSCHMANN; BAUMANN, 1991). Several studies have shown that exercise activates the release of neutrophil granule constituents into the circulation, indicating direct neutrophil activation in vivo. Elevated concentrations of neutrophil elastase have been detected in plasma after exercise (DUFAUX, ORDER, 1989a; BUSSE et al., 1980; CAMUS et al., 1992; HANSEN et al., 1991; KOKOT et al., 1988).

2.5 In vivo immunological methods

In vitro tests may not always provide accurate assessments of systemic immune responses; epidemiological studies may reflect concomitant conditions that have their own separate effects of immune function; and procedures involving animals may not represent reasonable models of human exercise. It is possible that the use of in vivo immunological methods may provide a tool to study clinically relevant immune changes. The systemic in vivo function of the immune system can be assessed using at least two different principles. The cellular immune response can be evaluated by evaluating the delayed hypersensitivity response to a recall antigen introduced to the skin. In that case an absent response (anergy) or a poor response indicate an impairment of the cellular immune response. The humoral immune response can be evaluated by the measurement of the specific antibody titres following vaccination. Low specific titres following antigen challenge would indicate a defective humoral response.

BRUUNSGAARD et al. (1997b) investigated whether an in vivo impairment of cell-mediated immunity and specific antibody production could be demonstrated after intense exercise of long duration (triathlon race). The cellular immune system was evaluated as the skin test response to seven recall antigens. The antigens were: Two toxoids (tetanus and diphteria), three bacterial (streptococcus, tuberculin, and proteus), and two fungal (candida and trichophyton). The humoral immune system was evaluated as the antibody response to pneumococcal polysaccharide vaccine, which is generally considered to be T cell independent, and two toxoids (tetanus and diphteria) that are dependent on T cells. The subjects had previously in life received tetanus and diphteria vaccinations but not pneumococcal vaccination. The protocol included twenty-two male triathletes, who performed one-half an ironman (group A). Vaccinations were given after the race and the skin test was applied. Specific antibody titers were measured before and 2 weeks after the race. The skin test was read 48 hours after application. Eleven non-exercising triathletes (group B) and 22 moderately trained men (group C) were used as controls. The cumulated skin test responses (sum of the diameters of indurations and number of positive skin spots) were significantly lower in group A compared with both groups B and C, whereas no differences were found between groups B and C. No differences were found between the groups regarding specific antibody titers against diphteria and tetanus toxoid or six pneumococcal antigens. The latter is in accordance with the findings by ESKOLA et al. (1978) and by PYNE and GLEESON (1997).The finding of a decreased cellular immunity following prolonged intense exercise may be a result of a decrease in the accumulation of cells or a result of a functional impairment including i.e. decreased production of IL-2 and IFN-gamma as suggested by WEINSTOCK et al. (1997).

3. Exercise and cytokines

Early studies suggesting that exercise induced a cytokine response were published in 1983 by CANNON and KLUGER (CANNON, KLUGER, 1983; CANNON et al., 1986; EVANS et al., 1986). The initial studies thus showed that systemic elevations of cytokines occur in serum after strenuous exercise. The identity of the observed cytokine was, however, uncertain. IL-6 has been detected in large amount during and after strenuous exercise (ULLUM et al., 1994a; SPRENGER et al., 1992; CASTELL et al., 1997; HELL-

STEN et al., 1997; NEHLSEN-CANARELLA et al., 1997; DRENTH et al., 1995; BRUUNS-GAARD et al., 1997a; OSTROWSKI et al., 1998a; OSTROWSKI et al., 1998b; OSTROWSKI et al., 1999; VENKATRAMAN, PENDERGAST, 1998). Several studies have failed to detect TNF-α after exercise (RIVIER et al., 1994; ULLUM et al., 1994a; SMITH et al., 1992; ULLUM et al., 1994b), whereas others report increased plasma TNF-a concentrations (DUFAUX, ORDER, 1989; ESPERSEN et al., 1990; OSTROWSKI et al., 1998b; OSTROWSKI et al., 1999). After a marathon race, TNF-α and IL-1 β increased two-fold, whereas the concentrations of IL-6 increased 50 folds; this was followed by a marked increase in the concentration of IL-1ra (OSTROWSKI et al.,

1998a). Recent studies show that several cytokines can be detected in plasma during and after strenuous exercise (OSTROWSKI et al., 1998a; OSTROWSKI et al., 1998b; OSTROWSKI et al., 1999), Fig.3. Thus strenuous exercise induces an increase in the pro-inflammatory cytokines TNF-α and IL-1β and a dramatic increase in the inflammation responsive cytokine IL-6. This release is balanced by the release of cytokine inhibitors (IL-1ra and TNF-receptors (TNF-R)) and the anti-inflammatory cytokine IL-10 (OSTROWSKI et al., 1999). These findings suggest that cytokine inhibitors and anti-inflammatory cytokines restrict the magnitude and duration of the inflammatory response to exercise. The presence of multiple cyto-

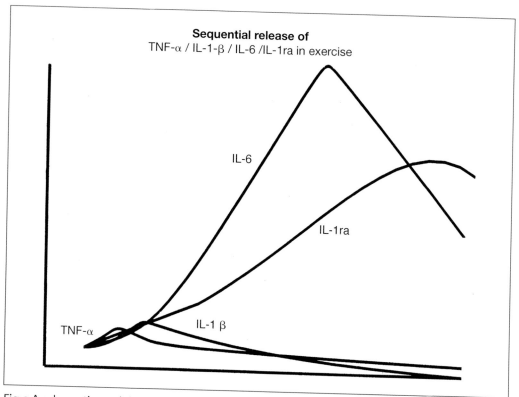

Sequential release of
TNF-α / IL-1-β / IL-6 /IL-1ra in exercise

IL-6

IL-1ra

TNF-α

IL-1 β

Fig.3 A schematic model on the cytokine response to exercise.

kines (TNF-α, IL-1β, IL-6, IL-2 receptors and interferon-g) in urine following exercise shows that the expression of a broad spectrum of cytokines in response to exercise is possible (SPRENGER et al., 1992).

4. Neuroendocrinological regulation

Studies where hormones were infused, hormone receptors were blocked by drugs, or the hormone production was inhibited by epidural blockade in relation to physical stress contribute to our understanding of the mechanisms of action. Based on these studies a model on the possible roles of stress hormones in exercise-induced immune changes can be proposed.

During exercise adrenaline is released from the adrenal medulla and noradrenaline is released from the sympathetic nerve terminals. Arterial plasma concentrations of adrenaline and noradrenaline increase almost linearly with duration of dynamic exercise and exponentially with intensity, when it is expressed relative to the individuals maximal oxygen uptake (KJAER, 1989). The expression of β-adrenoceptors on T, B and NK cells, macrophages and neutrophils in numerous species provide the molecular basis for these cells to be targets for catecholamine signaling (MADDEN; FELTEN, 1995). In humans, a single adrenaline injection induced transient increases in the number of circulating blood lymphocytes and monocytes and decreased the response to T cell mitogens (CRARY et al., 1983). Selective administration of adrenaline to obtain plasma-concentrations comparable to those obtained during concentric cycling for 1 hour at 75% of VO$_2$max, mimicked the exercise-induced effect on blood mononuclear cell subsets, NK cell activity, LAK cell activity and the lymphocyte proliferative response (KAPPEL et al., 1991; TVEDE et al., 1994; TONNESEN et al., 1987). However, adrenaline infusion caused a significantly smaller increase in neutrophil concentrations than that observed following exercise (KAPPEL et al., 1991; TVEDE et al., 1994).

AHLBORG and AHLBORG (1970) showed that after administration of propranolol, exercise resulted in practically no increase in lymphocyte concentration. Beta1+2-receptor blockade more than β1-blockade inhibited head-up tilt-induced lymphocytosis and the increase in the number of NK cells (KLOKKER et al., 1997b) is in accordance with the finding that primarily β2-receptors are expressed on lymphocytes (BENSCHOP et al., 1993). Beta-receptor blockade did not abolish the head-up tilt-induced neutrocytosis, which is in agreement with previous findings showing that adrenaline infusion caused smaller increase in neutrophil concentration than the exercise-induced increase (KAPPEL et al., 1991; TVEDE et al., 1994). The effect of noradrenaline on recruitment of lymphocytes to the blood resembles that of adrenaline (KAPPEL et al., 1998).

Plasma levels of pituitary hormones increase in response to exercise both with duration and intensity, however, the growth hormone response is more related to the peak exercise intensity rather than to duration of exercise or total work output (KJAER, 1992; VANHELDER et al., 1984). Addressing the question of a possible role of growth hormone in mediating acute exercise induced immune changes, KAPPEL et al. (1993) administered an in vivo injection of growth hormone in humans to obtain blood concentrations of growth hormone comparable with those observed during exercise. An intravenous bolus injection of growth hormone had no effect on BMNC subsets, NK cell activity, cytokine production, or lymphocyte function, but induced a highly significant neutrocytosis (KAPPEL et al., 1993). Therefore, growth hormone does not seem to play a major role in exercise-induced recruitment of lymphocytes to the blood. However, epinephrine and growth hormone in conjunction are probably responsible for the recruitment of neutrophils to the blood during physical stress.

It is not easy to rule out exactly what role β-endorphin has in exercise-induced immunomodulation. However, the available data indicates that β-endorphin is not responsible for the immediate recruitment of NK cells to the blood during acute exercise, but likely responsible for increased NK cell activity during chronic stress. This is based on the fact that NK cells are recruited to the blood immediately after the onset of exercise and even at exercise of very low intensity. Whereas the concentrations of β-endorphin increase only at high intensity and long duration exercise, which make it unlikely that β-endorphin plays a major immunomodulatory role in the immediate recruitment of NK cells to the blood. Furthermore, although FIATARONE et al. (1988) reported that naloxone blocked the exercise-induced increase in NK cell activity, the differences were, although statistically significant, small, and there was no effect of β-endorphin

receptor blockade on the number of cells. It has been found that β-endorphin receptor blockade during head-up tilt and inhibition of afferent nerves from working muscles which subsequently cause an increase in β-endorphin did not inhibit the recruitment of NK cells to the blood (KLOKKER et al., 1997a). This further supports the idea that β-endorphines do not play a role in the immediate recruitment of NK cells during acute exercise. The hypothesis that β-endorphin is important in maintaining increased NK cell activity during chronic stress is primarily based on the studies showing that voluntary chronic exercise augments in vivo natural immunity (JONSDOTTIR et al., 1996a). In addition β-endorphin and dynorphin in hypertensive rats (HOFFMANN et al., 1996; Persson et al., 1993; JONSDOTTIR et al., 1996b) and β-endorphin infusion, but not infusion of dynorphin to rats, increased the NK cell activity (JONSDOTTIR et al., 1996b). The concentrations of cortisol increases only in relation to exercise of long duration (GALBO, 1983). Thus short term exercise does not increase the cortisol concentration in plasma, and only minor changes in the concentrations of plasma cortisol was described in relation to acute time-limited exercise stress of 1 hour (GALBO, 1983).

Based on these studies we propose a model, Fig.2, on the possible roles of stress hormones in mediating exercise-related immune changes: Adrenaline and to a lesser degree noradrenaline are responsible for acute exercise-effects on lymphocyte subpopulations, NK and LAK cell activities. The increase in catecholamines and growth hormone mediates the acute effects on neutrophils, whereas cortisol exerts its effects within a time lag of at least two hours and contributes to maintain the lymphopenia and neutrocytosis only after long-term exercise. The role of β-endorphin is less clear, but we do not believe that β-endorphin plays an important role in the immediate recruitment of NK cells to the blood. We do hypothesize that β-endorphin is important in chronic stress. Stress hormones do not seem to be responsible for the exercise-induced increase in cytokines. This hypothesis is an extension of the hypothesis previously suggested by McCarthy and Dale (1988) that the immediate leukocytosis during exercise is attributable to elevated catecholamine levels, whereas the delayed neutrophilia is due to raised cortisol levels.

5. Is there a need for nutritional supplementation to avoid exercise-induced immunosuppression?

Given the fact the exercise induces dramatic changes in lymphocyte numbers and functions, it has been questioned if nutritional intervention would be able to abolish post-exercise induced immune changes. Reductions in plasma-glutamine concentrations due to muscular exercise has been hypothesized to influence lymphocyte function (Newsholme; Parry Billings, 1990). Altered plasma-glucose has also been implicated in decreasing stress-hormone levels and thereby influencing immune function (Nieman; Pedersen, 1999). Furthermore, free oxygen radicals and PG released by the elevated number of neutrophils and monocytes may influence the function of lymphocytes and contribute to the impaired function of the

later cells. Thus, nutritional supplementation with glutamine, carbohydrate, anti-oxidants or PG-inhibitors may in principle influence exercise-associated immune function.

It has generally been accepted that cells of the immune system obtain their energy by metabolism of glucose. However, it has been established that glutamine is also an important fuel for lymphocytes and macrophages (Newsholme, Parry Billings, 1990). Several lines of evidence suggest that glutamine is used at a very high rate by these cells, even when they are quiescent (Newsholme, 1994). It has been proposed that the glutamine pathway in lymphocytes may be under external regulation, due partly to the supply of glutamine itself (Newsholme, 1994). According to the "glutamine-hypothesis", under intense physical stress, such as exercise, the demands on muscle and other organs for glutamine are such that the lymphoid system may be forced into a glutamine debt. Thus, factors that directly or indirectly influence glutamine synthesis or release could theoretically influence the function of lymphocytes and monocytes (Newsholme, 1994; Newsholme, 1990). Following intense long-term exercise and other physical stress disorders, the glutamine concentration in plasma declines (Parry Billings et al., 1992; Keast et al., 1995; Essen et al., 1992; Lehmann et al., 1995) and low glutamine levels have been reported to be associated with overtraining (Rowbottom et al., 1996; Rowbottom et al., 1997). Although there is evidence that glutamine has an important role in lymphocyte function in vitro, recent placebo-controlled glutamine intervention studies (Rohde et al., 1998a; Rohde et al., 1998b) found that glutamine supplementation after the exercise abolished the post-exercise decline in plasma glutamine without influencing post-exercise immune impairment. Thus, there is little experimental support to the hypothesis that post-exercise decline in immune function is caused by a decrease in the plasma glutamine concentration. It was hypothesized that carbohydrate supplementation would maintain glucose concentrations and thereby diminish exercise-induced increases in stress hormones and immune function. This hypothesis has been tested in a number of studies (NEHLSEN-CANARELLA et al., 1997; NIEMAN et al., 1997b; MITCHELL et al., 1998; NIEMAN et al., 1998a; NIEMAN et al., 1998b) using double-blind, placebo-controlled randomized designs. Carbohydrate beverage ingestion before, during, and after 2.5 exercise was associated with higher plasma glucose levels, an attenuated cortisol and growth hormone response, fewer perturbations in blood immune cell counts, lower granulocyte and monocyte phagocytosis and oxidative burst activity, and a diminished pro- and anti-inflammatory cytokine response. However, carbohydrate ingestion has not been shown to abolish post-exercise immune impairment and the clinical significance remains to be determined. It has been suggested that if the n-6/n-3 ratio is shifted in favor of n-6, this will result in increased production of PGE and cellular immune suppression. Thus, during stress conditions n-3 fatty acids may counteract latent immunosuppression. Under the condition of hyper-metabolism n-3 fatty acids therefore potentially act to reduce the incidence of new infections. In animal experiments it was shown that the stress response following application of endotoxin, IL-1 or TNF was reduced when the animals were pretreated with n-3 fatty acids (fish oil) (JOHNSON et al., 1993).

In an animal experiment (mice), one group of animals received 18:3 (n-3) linseed oil. It was shown that linseed oil abolished post-exercise immunosuppression of the immunoglobulin M plaque forming cell response.

Anti-oxidants may in theory neutralize the reactive species which are produced by neutrophilic leukocytes during phagocytosis and as part as normal cellular respiration (HEMILA, 1992; BABIOR, 1984). There is limited evidence of the role of exogenous anti-oxidants (Vitamin C, Vitamin E) in modulating immune function in exercise and virtually no evidence on endogenous anti-oxidants. Using a double blind placebo design, the effect of Vitamin C on the incidence of URTI during the two week period following a marathon has been evaluated (PETERS et al., 1993). Vitamin C was reported to reduce the number of symptoms on upper respiratory tract infections, when supplementation began 3 weeks prior to the race. The same group (Peters et al., 1992) found that Vitamin A supplementation had no effect on the incidence of self-reported symptoms in marathoners. Vitamin C supplementation (NIEMAN et al., 1997a) had no effect on lymphocyte function and stress hormone levels.

Multiple endocrine and metabolic factors are involved in the exercise-induced immune changes (PEDERSEN et al., 1997). Therefore, in our opinion, it is unlikely that a single nutrient supplement will have physiologically relevant effects on exercise-induced immune modulation.

6. Chronic exercise

In contrast to the large number of studies on the immune response to acute exercise, much less is known concerning the effect of physical conditioning or training on immune function. This is largely due to the difficulties in separating fitness effects from the actual physical exercise. Thus, the changes induced by intense physical exercise may last at least 24 hours, and even moderate acute exercise induces significant immune changes for several hours. As it is not easy to persuade athletes to abstain from their normal training program even for just one day, it may be difficult to obtain results on true "resting levels". The influence of chronic exercise has been studied in both animal and human models, the latter including both longitudinal as well as cross-sectional studies. A good indicator of chronic exercise as a lifestyle factor, is to compare resting levels of the immune system in untrained controls and in athletes, who have been competing for several years. Two studies have been conducted on competitive male cyclists. In order to eliminate the effects of acute exercise in these studies, none of the subjects were allowed to exercise 20 hours prior to blood sampling. They all belonged to the elite Danish cycling group, they had been active in sports for a median of four years and had trained a medium of 20,000 km per year. In the first study the natural killer (NK) activity was measured in 27 highly trained cyclists and in 15 age- and sex-matched untrained controls. Median NK cell activity was 38.1% in trained group compared to 30.3% in untrained group (p = 0.008), and median % CD16+ NK cells was 17% in trained group versus

11% in untrained group (p = 0.007) (PEDERSEN et al., 1989). An additional study (TVEDE et al., 1991) examined the cellular immune system in 29 cyclists and 15 controls, measures were taken under resting conditions, during a period of low intensity training (winter). Fifteen cyclists and 10 controls were reexamined during a period of high intensity training (summer). The NK cell activity was significantly elevated in the trained group, both during the period of low intensity training (39.2% versus 30.9%) and during the period of high intensity training (55.2% versus 33.6%) (TVEDE et al., 1991). During low intensity training we found that the increased NK cell activity in trained subjects was due to an increased percentage of NK cells in these subjects. However, during high intensity training we found increased NK cell function in the trained subjects, despite a comparable number of circulating NK cells in trained subjects and controls. The mechanisms of this enhanced activity might be secondary to differences in NK cell activation. The results suggested that the NK cells were activated in trained subjects during high intensity training and that this may lead to an adjustment of the number of CD16+ cells in circulation by some unknown mechanism. In these studies (Tvede et al., 1991; Pedersen et al., 1989) other lymphocyte subpopulations and the lymphocyte proliferative responses did not differ among trained and untrained subjects.

Another study by NIEMAN et al. (1995b) supported the findings that athletes have increased NK cell activity. The study included 22 marathon runners who had completed at least seven marathons and had been training for marathon race events for at least four years. They were compared with a group of 18 sedentary controls. Despite a large difference between groups on VO$_2$max, percent body fat and physical activity, only the NK cell activity among the immune system variables measured emerged as being significantly different among the groups (higher among the marathoners). Concentrations of leucocytes and lymphocyte subsets as well as mitogen-stimulated proliferative responses did not differ significantly between the groups.

NIEMAN et al. (1993a) compared resting levels of several immune parameters in a group of 12 highly conditioned and 30 sedentary elderly women (67–85 years of age). The NK cell activity and phytohemagglutinin (PHA) stimulated proliferative responses were significantly elevated in the highly conditioned group compared with the inactive group.

In contrast to these studies BRAHMI et al. (1985) found no differences in NK cell activity, when they compared five trained males and 10 untrained females and males. Furthermore, NIEMAN et al. (1995a) compared 18 young male endurance athletes (10 runners and eight cyclists) with 11 nonathletic male adults and found no difference regarding NK cell activity. For all subjects combined there was no correlation between immune function and VO$_2$max.

The lymphocyte proliferative response has been described to be either decreased, (PAPA et al., 1989) elevated (NIEMAN et al., 1993; BAJ et al., 1994) or in most studies unchanged (PEDERSEN et al., 1989; Tvede et al., 1991; NIEMAN et al., 1995a; NIEMAN et al., 1995b; OSHIDA et al., 1988) when comparing athletes and non-athletes. The neutrophil func-

tion has been described to be either suppressed (LEWICKI et al., 1988; PYNE, 1994; AHLBORG, 1967) or not significantly different (HACK et al., 1992; Green et al., 1981) between trained and untrained groups. BAJ et al. (1994) and HACK et al. (1994) found that the neutrophil function was unchanged in athletes during a low training period, but decreased during periods of high intensity training. Thus, there is a tendency towards decreased neutrophil function in athletes during periods of high intensity training.

The effect of chronic exercise has been studied in longitudinal designs. This is advantageous as the studies use randomization, thus in principle excluding confounding factors. The disadvantage is that the majority of studies investigate the effect on the immune system of at most 16 weeks of training, whereas the cross sectional studies reflect many years of training. All studies, however, show significant effects on VO$_2$max as a result of training.

NIEMAN et al. (1993a) found no influence on NK cell activity or any other immune parameters, when 30 elderly women were randomized into a 12 week walking program, whereas CRIST et al. (1989) found that treadmill exercise for 16 weeks enhanced the NK cell activity in elderly women. In another study, NIEMAN et al. (1990b) found that 15 weeks of walking enhanced the NK cell activity in moderately obese, previously inactive women. When 18 patients with rheumatoid arthritis were allocated to an eight week cycling program, it was found that chronic exercise had no effect on the NK cell activity, lymphocyte proliferative responses, concentrations or proportions of lymphocyte subpopulation or cytokine production (BARNES et al.,

1991). Furthermore, exercise had no influence on erythrocyte sedimentation rate, C reactive protein, or number of swollen and tender joints. However, using a visual analog scale it was shown that the patients who had performed the exercise program had less pain, less morning stiffness and were less fatigued. MacNeil and Hoffman-Goetz (1993a; 1993b) investigated the influence of nine weeks of chronic exercise on natural cytotoxicity in male C3H mice. Both in vivo cytotoxicity (pulmonary vasculature) and in vitro cytotoxicity (spleen) were determined for voluntary (wheel running) and forced (treadmill running, 15m/min, 30 min/day) training. A sedentary control group and a treadmill control group (5m/min, 5 min/day) were included. Forced and voluntary chronic exercise enhanced in vivo as well as in vitro cytotoxic activity, but elevated cytotoxicity was not found in either of the control groups. Several studies from the same group, using training protocols of varying length and intensity and different animal species, support the findings showing increased resting levels of natural cytotoxicity after voluntary exercise (Hoffman-Goetz et al., 1994; Hoffman-Goetz et al., 1992; MacNeil, Hoffman-Goetz, 1993; MacNeil, Hoffman-Goetz, 1993).

Lin et al. (1993) examined the effect of chronic exercise training in rats, who were trained on a drum exerciser at the intensity of 60–70% of VO_2max for 30 min and then extended up to 60 min per day, five days per week. The rats were at rest three days before sacrifice, and it was found that the IL-2 production was suppressed in the training group.

NK cell activity is increased in athletes versus non-athletes, however, in randomized, longitudinal studies chronic training has not shown a consistent effect on NK cell activity. This may be explained by the following: In order to become a successful athlete, good health is an absolute necessity. Thus the level of natural immunity may select who will be an athlete and who will not, and the cross-sectional studies may in theory simply reflect this selection. However, whereas the longitudinal training studies in humans fail to show consistent effects on natural immunity, most animal studies have shown that chronic exercise enhances resting levels of natural cytotoxic activity. The latter indicates a true relationship, not just an association, between NK cell activity and chronic exercise. Thus, a high level of resting natural immunity exists in trained individuals. How do we than explain that elite athletes as a group are more prone to upper respiratory tract infections than their sedentary counterparts? The most likely explanation is that the increased susceptibility to infections is due to post-exercise suppression of NK and B cell functions. During this post-exercise temporary immunosuppression (Pedersen; Ullum, 1994) there is an "open window" of opportunity for pathogens (Brines et al., 1996). In a recent review on the regulation of neutrophil function during exercise, Pyne (1994) suggests that repetitive high-intensity training sessions by elite athletes may leave a significant proportion of their circulating neutrophils in a chronically refractory state. This may also explain the observation that elite athletes, as a group, are more susceptible to infections (Nieman, 1996b).

7. Upper respiratory tract infections

It has been demonstrated in a number of studies that resting levels of the immune system are not impaired in trained versus untrained; this has recently been reviewed (NIEMAN, 1996). However, based on anecdotal information a general feeling has been that while regular training promotes resistance to upper respiratory tract infections (URTI) severe exertion, especially when coupled with mental stress places athletes at increased risk for URTI (FITZGERALD, 1991; NIEMAN, 1994).

PETERS and BATEMAN (1983) carried out a prospective study of the incidence of symptoms of URTI in 150 randomly selected runners who took part in the 1982 Two Oceans Marathon in Cape Town, and compared this with the incidence in individually matched controls who did not run. Runners were questioned on the day before and two weeks after the race. Symptoms of URTI occurred in 33.3% of runners compared with 15.3% of controls, and were most common in those who achieved the faster race times. NIEMAN et al. (1989) studied the incidence of infectious episodes in 273 runners during a two month training period prior to a 5km, 10 km or half-marathon race. In addition the effect of the race experience on infectious episodes was studied. Only 6.8% of the runners preparing for the half-marathon race reported becoming sick versus 17.95% of the 5km and 10 km runners (p = 0.067). This study thus showed a trend that runners with a more serious commitment to regular exercise had less infectious episodes.

The largest epidemiological study on exercise and URTI was performed by Nieman et al. (1990a) who researched the incidence of URTI in a group of 2311 marathon runners who took part in the 1987 Los Angeles Marathon race. It was found that 12.9% of Los Angeles Marathon participants reported an infectious episode during the week following the race in comparison to only 2.2% of similarly experienced runners who had applied but did not participate (for reasons other than sickness). Controlling important demographic and training data by using logistic regression, it was determined that the odds were 6 to 1 in favor of sickness for the marathon race participants versus the nonparticipating runners.

There are a lack of studies comparing URTI in large groups of moderately active individuals. However, two randomized experimental trials using small numbers of subjects have provided important data in support of the viewpoint that moderate physical activity may reduce URTI symptoms. A study on 36 women who performed a 15 week walking program (45 min of walking, 5 days per week) reported significantly fewer days with URTI symptoms during the 15 week study than in the control group (5.1 versus 10.8 days). The number of separate URTI did not vary between groups, but the number of URTI symptom days per incident was lower in the exercising group (NIEMAN et al., 1990b). In a randomized, controlled study of elderly women, 67–85 years of age, the incidence of the common cold during a 12 week period in the fall was measured to be the lowest in highly conditioned subjects who exercised moderately each day for about 1.5 hour (8%), elderly subjects who walked 40 min, 5 times per week had an incidence of 21%, compared with 50% for

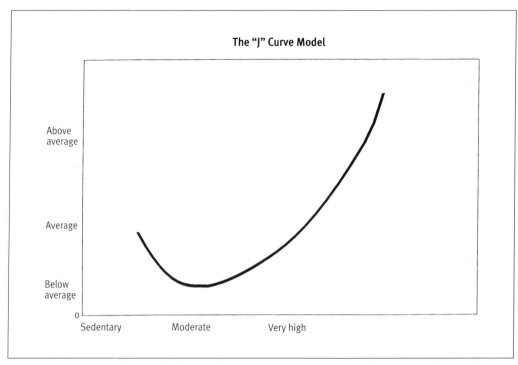

Fig. 4. „J"-shaped model of relationship between varying amounts of exercise and risk of upper respiratory tract infection (URTI). This model suggests that moderate exercise may lower risk of respiratory infection while excessive amounts may increase risk.

the sedentary control group (NIEMAN et al., 1993a). This study clearly showed that elderly women, not engaging in cardiorespiratory exercise are more likely to experience an URTI during the fall season than those who do not exercise regularly.

Based on the above mentioned epidemiological studies a relationship between exercise and URTI has been modeled in the form of „J" curve, Fig.4. This model suggests that while the risk of URTI may decrease below that of sedentary individual when one engages in moderate exercise training, risk may rise above average during periods of excessive amount of high-intensity exercise (NIEMAN, 1994).

8. Exercise and cancer

Based on several epidemiological studies, there are accumulating substantial evidence for a protective role of exercise in colon cancer and breast cancer risk (PEDERSEN, CLEMMENSEN, 1997). Although there are the same trend in prostate cancer, it is too premature to draw strong conclusions regarding a potential effect of exercise (PEDERSEN, CLEMMENSEN, 1997). The role of exercise in tumorigenesis is probably based on multiple and overlapping mechanisms of action. These include altered peristalsis, bile acid composition, diets, prostaglandins and cytokines. Exercise is known to induce dramatic changes in hormonal factors and may thereby exert its effect on tumor growth. The exercise-induced effect on sex hormones may directly influence the tumor growth of some cancers such as breast cancer and prostate cancer. However, experimental evidence also suggests that estrogens may influence tumor growth by natural immune suppression (HANNA; SCHNEIDER, 1983). Certainly, exercise induces dramatic changes in neuroendocrine factors, which again cause alterations in the cellular immune system, especially in natural immunity. There is, however, a clear need for well-designed investigations to address the putative interactions among exercise, natural immunity and cancer. A common assumption is that because chronic training enhances natural immunity, the mechanism for reduced tumor growth is enhanced natural immunity. This approach has, however, not been experimentally invalidated. The epidemiological evidence concerning breast cancer in women and the protective effect of physical activity have been reviewed elsewhere (HOFFMAN-GOETZ, HUSTED, 1994; FRIEDENREICH, ROHAN, 1995; HOFFMAN-GOETZ, HUSTED, 1995). Regarding the acute exercise effects on the immune response, it has been shown that natural immunity is enhanced during moderate exercise and severe exercise. However, the numbers and function of cells mediating cytotoxic activity against tumor target cells are suppressed after intense, long-term exercise. In accordance to the immune surveillance theory, it therefore was to be expected that moderate exercise protected against malignancy whereas exhaustive exercise was linked with increased cancer risk. Today there are limited data to support this theory.

Although the majority of epidemiological studies show that physical activity as such protects against cancer, there are until now no published data on increased cancer risk in association with exhaustive training.

9. The open window hypothesis

In essence the immune system is enhanced during moderate and severe exercise, and only intense long-duration exercise is followed by immunodepression. The latter include suppressed concentration of lymphocytes, suppressed non-MHC-restriced cytotoxicity (NK and LAK cell activity) and secretory IgA in mucosa. During the time of immunodepression referred to as "the open window", microbacterial agents, especially virus may invade the host and infections may be established. One reason for the "overtraining effect" seen in elite athletes could be that this window of opportunism for pathogens is longer and the degree of immunosuppression more pronounced, Fig. 1. Based on the available data a model on exercise, duration and intensity is suggested. NK cells and other lymphocytes are recruited to the blood from a pool. This pool may be located in various organs such as the spleen, the lungs, the bone marrow and the lymph nodes. The number of cells that enter the circulation are determined by the intensity of the stimulus. If it has been a long lasting and very intense stimulus the total concentration of lymphocytes decline. This may in part be ascribed to a redistribution of lymphocytes to organs. Whether or not "the open window" in the immune system occurs is thus dependent on the intensity and duration of exercise and somewhat dependent on recovery periods. It remains to be shown whether prophylactic treatment with amino acid combinations, anti-oxidant, prostaglandin inhibitors or other nutrients will diminish or abolish post-exercise suppression, thus if "the open window" can be closed. It has recently been suggested that neutrophils serve as a last line of defense. During "the open window" immune suppression of lymphoid cells, neutrophils are being mobilised to plug this gaps. The removal of this back-up system following extreme activity would be compatible with the propensity of "overtrained" individuals to develop upper respiratory infections (BRINES et al., 1996).

ACKNOWLEDGEMENT: The work was supported by The National Research Foundation 504–14.

References

AHLBORG, B. (1967): Leukocytes in blood during prolonged physical exercise. In: *Forsvarsmedicin, 3,* 36–48.

AHLBORG, B.; AHLBORG, G. (1970): Exercise leukocytosis with and without beta-adrenergic blockade. In: *Acta Medica Scandinavica, 187,* 241–246.

BABIOR, B. M. (1984): Oxidants from phagocytes: agents of defense and destruction. In: *Blood, 64,* 959–966.

BAJ, Z.; KANTORSKI, J.; MAJEWSKA, E.; ZEMAN, K.; POKOCA, L.; FORNALCZYK, E. et al. (1994): Immunological status of competitive cyclists before and after the training season. In: *International Journal of Sports Medicine, 15,* 319–324.

BARNES, C. A.; FORSTER, M. J.; FLESHNER, M.; AHANOTU, E. N.; LAUDENSLAGER, M. L.; MAZZEO, R. S. et al. (1991): Exercise does not modify spatial memory, brain autoimmunity, or antibody response in aged F-344 rats. In: *Neurobiology of Aging, 12,* 47–53.

BENSCHOP, R. J.; OOSTVEEN, F. G.; HEIJNEN, C. J.; BALLIEUX, R. E. (1993): Beta 2-adrenergic stimulation causes detachment of natural killer cells from cultured endothelium. In: *European Journal of Immunology, 23,* 3242–3247.

BIERMAN, H. R.; KELLY, K. H.; CORDES, F. L.; PETRAKIS, N. L.; KASS, H.; SHPIL, E. L. (1952): The influence of respiratory movements upon the circulating leukocytes. In: *Blood, 7,* 533–544.

BRAHMI, Z.; THOMAS, J. E.; PARK, M.; DOWDESWELL, I. R. (1985): The effect of acute exercise on natural killer-cell activity of trained and sedentary human subjects. In: *Journal of Clinical Immunologie, 5,* 321–328.

BRINES, R.; HOFFMAN-GOETZ, L.; PEDERSEN, B. K. (1996): Can you exercise to make your immune system fitter? In: *Immunology Today, 17,* 252–254.

BRUNDA, M. J.; HERBERMAN, R. B.; HOLDEN, H. T. (1980): Inhibition of murine natural killer cell activity by prostaglandins. In: *Immunopharmacology, 124,* 2682–2687.

BRUUNSGAARD, H.; GALBO, H.; HALKJAER-KRISTENSEN, J.; JOHANSEN, T. L.; MACLEAN, D. A.; PEDERSEN, B. K. (1997a): Exercise-induced increase in interleukin-6 is related to muscle damage. In: *Journal of Physiology London, 499,* 833–841.

BRUUNSGAARD, H.; HARTKOPP, A.; MOHR, T.; KONRADSEN, H.; HERON, I.; MORDHORST, C. H. et al. (1997b): In vivo cell mediated immunity and vaccination response following prolonged, intense exercise. In: *Medicine and Science in Sports and Exercise, 29,* 1176-1181.

BUSCHMANN, H.; BAUMANN, M. (1991): Alterations of cellular immune response during intensive training of event horses. In: *Zentralblatt für Veterinärmedizin, 38,* 90–94.

BUSSE, W. W.; ANDERSON, C. L.; HANSON, P. G.; FOLTS, J. D. (1980): The effect of exercise on the granulocyte response to isoproterenol in the trained athlete and unconditioned individual. In: *Journal of Allergy and Clinical Immunology, 65,* 358–364.

CAMUS, G.; PINCEMAIL, J.; LEDENT, M.; JUCHMES FERIR, A.; LAMY, M.; DEBY DUPONT, G. et al. (1992): Plasma levels of poly-morphonuclear elastase and myelo-peroxidase after uphill walking and down-hill running at similar energy cost. In: *International Journal of Sports Medicine, 13,* 443–446.

CANNON, J. G.; EVANS, W. J.; HUGHES, V. A.; MEREDITH, C. N.; DINARELLO, C. A. (1986): Physiological mechanisms contributing to increased interleukin-1 secretion. In: *Journal of Applied Physiology, 61,* 1869–1874.

CANNON, J. G.; KLUGER, M. J. (1983): Endogenous pyrogen activity in human plasma after exercise. In: *Science, 220,* 617–619.

CASTELL, L. M.; POORTMANS, J. R.; LECLERCQ, R.; BRASSEUR, M.; DUCHATEAU, J.; NEWSHOLME, E. A. (1997): Some aspects of the acute phase response after a marathon race, and the effects of glutamine supplementation. In: *European Journal of Applied Physiology and Occupational, 75,* 47–53.

CRARY, B.; BORYSENKO, M.; SUTHERLAND, D. C.; KUTZ, I.; BORYSENKO, J. Z. BENSON, H. (1983): Decrease in mitogen responsiveness of mononuclear cells from peripheral blood after epinephrine administration in humans. In: *Immunopharmacology, 130,* 694–697.

CRIST, D. M.; MACKINNON, L. T.; THOMPSON, R. F.; ATTERBOM, H. A.; EGAN, P. A. (1989): Physical exercise increases natural cellular-mediated tumor cytotoxity in elderly women. In: *Gerontology, 35,* 66–71.

DRENTH, J. P.; VAN UUM, S. H.; VAN DEUREN, M.; PESMAN, G. J.; VAN DER VEN JONGEKRUG, J.; VAN DER MEER, J. W. (1995): Endurance run increases circulating IL-6 and IL-1ra but downregulates ex vivo TNF-alpha and IL-1beta production. In: *Journal of Applied Physiology, 79,* 1497–1503.

DUFAUX, B.; ORDER, U. (1989a): Plasma elastase-alpha 1-antitrypsin, neopterin, tumor necrosis factor, and soluble interleukin-2 receptor after prolonged exercise. In: *International Journal of Sports Medicine, 10,* 434–438.

DUFAUX, B.; ORDER, U. (1989b): Complement activation after prolonged exercise. In: *Clinical Chimica Acta, 179,* 45–49.

ESKOLA, J.; RUUSKANEN, O.; SOPPI, E.; VILJANEN, M. K.; JARVINEN, M.; TOIVONEN, H. et al. (1978): Effect of sport stress on lymphocyte transformation and antibody formation. In: *Clinical and Experimental Immunology, 32,* 339–345.

ESPERSEN, G. T.; ELBAEK, A.; ERNST, E.; TOFT, E.; KAALUND, S.; JERSILD, C. et al. (1990): Effect of physical exercise on cytokines and lymphocyte subpopulations in human peripheral blood. In: *APMIS, 98,* 395–400.

ESSEN, P.; WERNERMAN, J.; SONNENFELD, T.; THUNELL, S.; VINNARS, E. (1992): Free amino acids in plasma and muscle during 24 hours post- operatively-a descriptive study. In: *Clinical Physiology, 12,* 163–177.

EVANS, W. J.; MEREDITH, C. N.; CANNON, J. G.; DINARELLO, C. A.; FRONTERA, W. R.; HUGHES, V. A. et al. (1986): Metabolic changes following eccentric exercise in trained and untrained men. In: *Journal of Applied Physiology, 61,* 1864–1868.

FIATARONE, M. A.; MORLEY, J. E.; BLOOM, E. T.; BENTON, D.; MAKINODAN, T.; SOLOMON, G. F. (1988): Endogenous opioids and the exercise-induced augmentation of natural killer cell activity. In: *Journal of Laboratory and Clinical Medicine, 112,* 544–552.

FITZGERALD, L. (1988): Exercise and the immune system. In: *Immunology Today, 9,* 337–339.

FITZGERALD, L. (1991): Overtraining increases the susceptibility to infection. In: *International Journal of Sports Medicine, 12,* 5–8.

FRIEDENREICH, C. M.; ROHAN, T. E. (1995): A review of physical activity and breast cancer. In: *Epidemiology, 6,* 311–317.

GALBO, H. (1983): Hormonal and metabolic adaption to exercise. New York: Thieme Verlag. 1–117.

GLEESON, M.; MCDONALD, W. A.; PYNE, D. B.; CRIPPS, A. W.; FRANCIS, J. L.; FRICKER, P. A. et al. (1999): Salivary IgA levels and infection risk in elite swimmers. In: *Medicine and Science in Sports and Exercise, 31,* 63–73.

GREEN, R. L.; KAPLAN, S. S.; RABIN, B. S.; STANITSKI, C. L.; ZDZIARSKI, U. (1981): Immune function in marathon runners. In: *Annals of Allergy, 47,* 73–75.

GRIMM, E. A.; MAZUMDER, A.; ZHANG, H. Z.; ROSENBERG, S. A. (1982): Lymphokine-activated killer cell phenomenon. Lysis of natural killer-resistant fresh solid tumor cells by interleukin-2-activated autologous human peripheral blood lymphocytes. In: *Journal of Experimental Medicine, 155,* 1823–1841.

HACK, V.; STROBEL, G.; RAU, J. P.; WEICKER, H. (1992): The effect of maximal exercise on the activity of neutrophil granulocytes in highly trained athletes in a moderate training period. In: *European Journal of Applied Physiology, 65,* 520–524.

HACK, V.; STROBEL, G.; WEISS, M.; WEICKER, H. (1994): PMN cell counts and phagocytic activity of highly trained athletes depend on training period. In: *Journal of Applied Physiology, 77,* 1731–1735.

HANNA, N.; SCHNEIDER, M. (1983): Enhancement of tumor metastasis and suppression of natural killer cell activity by beta-estradiol treatment. In: *Journal of Immunology, 130,* 974–980.

HANSEN, J. B.; WILSGARD, L.; OSTERUD, B. (1991): Biphasic changes in leukocytes induced by strenuous exercise. In: *European Journal of Applied Physiology, 62,* 157–161.

HELLSTEN, Y.; FRANDSEN, U.; ORTHENBLAD, N.; SJODIN, N.; RICHTER, E. A. (1997): Xanthine oxidase in human skeletal muscle following eccentric exercise: a role of inflammation. In: *Journal of Physiology (London Then Cambridge), 498,* 239–248.

HEMILA, H. (1992): Vitamin C and the common cold. In: *British Journal of Nutrition, 67,* 3–16.

HOFFMAN-GOETZ, L.; ARUMUGAM, Y.; SWEENY, L. (1994): Lymphokine activated killer cell activity following voluntary physical activity in mice. In: *Journal of Sports Medicine and Physical Fitness, 34,* 83–90.

HOFFMAN-GOETZ, L.; HUSTED, J. (1994): Exercise and breast cancer: review and critical analysis of the literature. In: *Canadian Journal of Applied Physiology, 19,* 237–252.

HOFFMAN-GOETZ, L.; HUSTED, J. (1995): Exercise and cancer: do the biology and epidemiology correspond? In: *Exercise Immunology Review, 1,* 81–96.

HOFFMAN-GOETZ, L.; MACNEIL, B.; ARUMUGAM, Y.; RANDALL SIMPSON, J. (1992): Differential effects of exercise and housing condition on murine natural killer cell activity and tumor growth. In: *International Journal of Sports Medicine, 13,* 167–171.

HOFFMAN-GOETZ, L.; PEDERSEN, B. K. (1994): Exercise and the immune system: a model of the stress response? In: *Immunology Today, 15,* 382–387.

HOFFMAN-GOETZ, L.; PEDERSEN, B. K. (2000): Physiological Reviews 80, 1055–1081.

HOFFMANN, P.; TERENIUS, L.; THOREN, P. (1996): Cerebrospinal fluid immunoreactive exercise in spontaneously hypertensive rat. In: *Regulatory Peptides, 28,* 233–239.

HOUSH, T. J.; JOHNSON, G. O.; HOUSH, D. J.; EVANS, S. L.; THARP, G. D. (1991): The effect of exercise at various temperatures on salivary levels of immunoglobulin A. In: *International Journal of Sports Medicine, 12,* 498–500.

JOHNSON, J. A. 3D; GRISWOLD, J. A.; MUAKKASSA, F. F. (1993): Essential fatty acids influence survival in sepsis. In: *Journal of Trauma, 35,* 128–131.

JONSDOTTIR, I. H.; ASEA, A.; HOFFMANN, P.; DAHLGREN, U. I.; ANDERSSON, B.; HELLSTRAND, K. et al. (1996a): Voluntary chronic exercise augments in vivo natural immunity in rats. In: *Journal of Applied Physiology, 80,* 1799–1803.

JONSDOTTIR, I. H.; JOHANSSON, C.; ASEA, A.; HELLSTRAND, K.; THOREN, P.; HOFFMANN, P.

(1996b): Chronic intracerebrovascular administration of Beta-endorphin augments natural killer cell cytotoxicity in rats. In: *Regulatory Peptides, 62,* 113–118.

KAPPEL, M.; HANSEN, M. B.; DIAMANT, M.; JORGENSEN, J. O.; GYHRS, A.; PEDERSEN, B. K. (1993): Effects of an acute bolus growth hormone infusion on the human immune system. In: *Hormone and Metabolic Research, 25,* 579–585.

KAPPEL, M.; POULSEN, T.; GALBO, H.; PEDERSEN, B. K. (1998): Effect of norepinephrine infusion on immune parameters. In: *European Journal of Applied Physiology, 79,* 93–98.

KAPPEL, M.; TVEDE, N.; GALBO, H.; HAAHR, P. M.; KJAER, M.; LINSTOW, M. et al. (1991): Evidence that the effect of physical exercise on NK cell activity is mediated by epinephrine. In: *Journal of Applied Physiology, 70,* 2530–2534.

KEAST, D.; ARSTEIN, D.; HARPER, W.; FRY, R. W.; MORTON, A. R. (1995): Depression of plasma glutamine concentration after exercise stress and its possible influence on the immune system. In: *Medical Journal of Australia, 162,* 15–18.

KJAER, M. (1989): Epinephrine and some other hormonal responses to exercise in man: with special reference to physical training. In: *International Journal of Sports Medicine, 10,* 2–15.

KJAER, M. (1992): Regulation of hormonal during exercise and metabolic responses in humans. In: *Exercise and Sport Sciences Reviews, 20,* 161–184.

KLOKKER, M.; SECHER, N. H.; MADSEN, P.; OLESEN, H. L.; WARBERG, J.; PEDERSEN, B. K. (1997a): Influence of naloxone on the cellular immune response to head-up tilt in humans. In: *European Journal of Applied Physiology, 76,* 415–420.

KLOKKER, M.; SECHER, N. H.; OLESEN, H. L.; MADSEN, P.; WARBERG, J.; PEDERSEN, B. K. (1997b): Adrenergic beta-1+2 receptor blockade suppresses the natural killer cell response during head-up tilt. In: *Journal of Applied Physiology, 83,* 1492–1498.

KOKOT, K.; SCHAEFER, R. M.; TESCHNER, M.;

GILGE, U.; PLASS, R.; HEIDLAND, A. (1988): Activation of leukocytes during prolonged physical exercise. In: *Advances in Experimental Medicine and Biology, 240,* 57–63.

KUROKAWA, Y.; SHINKAI, S.; TORII, J.; HINO, S.; SHEK, P. N. (1995): Exercise-induced changes in the expression of surface adhesion molecules on circulating granulocytes and lymphocytes subpopulations. In: *European Journal of Applied Physiology, 71,* 245–252.

LEHMANN, M.; HUONKER, M.; DIMEO, F.; HEINZ, N.; GASTMANN, U.; TREIS, N. et al. (1995): Serum amino acid concentrations in nine athletes before and after the 1993 Colmar ultra triathlon. In: *International Journal of Sports Medicine, 16,* 155–159.

LEWICKI, R.; TCHORZEWSKI, H.; DENYS, A.; KOWALSKA, M.; GOLINSKA, A. (1987): Effect of physical exercise on some parameters of immunity in conditioned sportsmen. In: *International Journal of Sports Medicine, 8,* 309–314.

LEWICKI, R.; TCHORZEWSKI, H.; MAJEWSKA, E.; NOWAK, Z.; BAJ, Z. (1988): Effect of Maximal Physical Exercise on T-Lymphocyte Subpopulations and on Interleukin 1 (IL 1) – and Interleukin 2 (IL2) – Production in Vitro. In: *International Journal of Sports Medicine, 9,* 114–117.

LIEW, F. Y.; RUSSELL, S. M.; APPLEYARD, G.; BRAND, C. M.; BEALE, J. (1984): Cross-protection in mice infected with influenza A virus by the respiratory route is correlated with local IgA antibody rather than serum antibody or cytotoxic T cell reactivity. In: *European Journal of Immunology, 14,* 350–356.

LIN, Y. S.; JAN, M. S.; CHEN, H. I. (1993): The effect of chronic and acute exercise on immunity in rats. In: *International Journal of Sports Medicine, 14,* 86–92.

MACKINNON, L. T.; CHICK, T. W.; VAN AS, A.; TOMASI, T. B. (1987): The effect of exercise on secretory and natural immunity. In: *Advances in Experimental Medicine and Biology, 216A,* 869–876.

MACKINNON, L. T.; HOOPER, S. (1994):

Mucosal (secretory) immune system responses to exercise of varying intensity and during overtraining. In: *International Journal of Sports Medicine, 15*, 179–183.

MacNeil, B.; Hoffman-Goetz, L. (1993a): Chronic exercise enhances in vivo and in vitro cytotoxic mechanisms of natural immunity in mice. In: *Journal of Applied Physiology, 74*, 388–395.

MacNeil, B.; Hoffman-Goetz, L. (1993b): Effect of exercise on natural cytotoxicity and pulmonary tumor metastases in mice. In: *Medicine and Science in Sports and Exercise, 25*, 922–928.

MacNeil, B.; Hoffman-Goetz, L. (1993c): Exercise training and tumor metastasis in mice: influence of time of exercise onset. In: *Anticancer Research, 13*, 2085–2088.

Madden, K.; Felten, D. L. (1995): Experimental basis for neural-immune interactions. In: *Physiological Research, 75*, 77–106.

McCarthy, D. A.; Dale, M. M. (1988): The leucocytosis of exercise. A review and model. In: *Sports Medicine, 6*, 333–363.

McDowell, S. L.; Chaloa, K.; Housh, T. J.; Tharp, G. D.; Johnson, G. O. (1991): The effect of exercise intensity and duration on salivary immunoglobulin A. In: *European Journal of Applied Physiology, 63*, 108–111.

McDowell, S. L.; Hughes, R. A.; Hughes, R. J.; Housh, D. J.; Housh, T. J.; Johnson, G. O. (1992): The effect of exhaustive exercise on salivary immunoglobulin A. In: *Journal of Sports Medicine and Physical Fitness, 32*, 412–415.

Mitchell, J. B.; Pizza, F. X.; Paquet, B. J.; Davis, B. J.; Forrest, M. B.; Braun, W. A. (1998): Influence of carbohydrate status on immune responses before and after endurance exercise. In: *Journal of Applied Physiology, 84*, 1917–1925.

Muns, G.; Liesen, H.; Riedel, H.; Bergman, K. C. (1989): Influence of long-distance running on IgA in nasal secretion and saliva. In: *Deutsche Zeitschrift für Sportmedizin, 40*, 94–99.

Nash, H. L. (1987): Can exercise make us immune to disease? In: *Physician and Sportsmedicine*, 250–253.

Nehlsen-Canarella, S. L.; Fagoaga, O. R.; Nieman, D. C. (1997): Carbohydrate and the cytokine response to 2.5 hours of running. In: *Journal of Applied Physiology, 82*, 1662–1667.

Newsholme, E. A. (1990): Psychoimmunology and cellular nutrition: an alternative hypothesis [editorial]. In: *Biological Psychiatry, 27*, 1–3.

Newsholme, E. A. (1994): Biochemical mechanisms to explain immunosuppression in well-trained and overtrained athletes. In: *International Journal of Sports Medicine, 15*, 142–147.

Newsholme, E. A.; Parry Billings, M. (1990): Properties of glutamine release from muscle and its importance for the immune system. In: *Journal of Parenteral and Enteral Nutrition, 14*, 63–67.

Nielsen, H. B.; Secher, N. H.; Kappel, M.; Hanel, B.; Pedersen, B. K. (1996): Lymphocyte, N. K.; and LAK cell responses to maximal exercise. In: *International Journal of Sports Medicine, 17*, 60–65.

Nieman, D. C. (1994a): Exercise, upper respiratory tract infection, and the immune system. In: *Medicine and Science in Sports and Exercise, 26*, 128–139.

Nieman, D. C. (1994b): Exercise, infection, and immunity. In: *International Journal of Sports Medicine, 15 Suppl., 3*, 131–141.

Nieman, D. C. (1996): Prolonged aerobic exercise, immune response, and risk of infection. In: *Exercise and immune function.* Edited by L Hoffman- Goetz. CRC Press. 143-162.

Nieman, D. C.; Brendle, D.; Henson, D. A.; Suttles, J.; Cook, V. D.; Warren, B. J. et al. (1995a): Immune function in athletes versus nonathletes. In: *International Journal of Sports Medicine, 16*, 329–333.

Nieman, D. C.; Buckley, K. S.; Henson, D. A.; Warren, B. J.; Suttles, J.; Ahle, J. C. et al. (1995b): Immune function in marathon runners versus sedentary controls. In: *Medicine and Science in Sports and Exercise, 27*, 986–992.

Nieman, D. C.; Henson, D. A. (1994): Role of endurance exercise in immune senescence. In: *Medicine and Science in Sports and Exercise, 26,* 172–181.

NIEMAN, D. C.; HENSON, D. A.; BUTTERWORTH, D. E.; WARREN, B. J.; DAVIS, J. M.; FAGOAGA, O. R. et al. (1997a): Vitamin C supplementation does not alter the immune response to 2.5 hours of running. In: *International Journal of Sport Nutrition, 7,* 173–184

NIEMAN, D. C.; HENSON, D. A.; GARNER, E. B.; BUTTERWORTH, D. E.; WARREN, B. J.; UTTER, A. et al. (1997b): Carbohydrate affects natural killer cell redistribution but not activity after running. In: *Medicine and Science in Sports and Exercise, 29,* 1318–1324.

NIEMAN, D. C.; HENSON, D. A.; GUSEWITCH, G.; WARREN, B. J.; DOTSON, R. C.; BUTTERWORTH, D. E. et al. (1993a): Physical activity and immune function in elderly women. In: *Medicine and Science in Sports and Exercise, 25,* 823–831.

NIEMAN, D. C.; JOHANSSEN, L. M.; LEE, J. W. (1989): Infectious episodes in runners before and after a roadrace. In: *Journal of Sports Medicine and Physical Fitness, 29,* 289–296.

NIEMAN, D. C.; JOHANSSEN, L. M.; LEE, J. W.; ARABATZIS, K. (1990a): Infectious episodes in runners before and after the Los Angeles Marathon. In: *Journal of Sports Medicine and Physical Fitness, 30,* 316–328.

NIEMAN, D. C.; MILLER, A. R.; HENSON, D. A.; WARREN, B. J.; GUSEWITCH, G.; JOHNSON, R. L. et al. (1993b): Effects of high- vs. moderate-intensity exercise on natural killer cell activity. In: *Medicine and Science in Sports and Exercise, 25,* 1126–1134.

NIEMAN, D. C.; NEHLSEN CANNARELLA, S. L.; MARKOFF, P. A.; BALK LAMBERTON, A. J.; YANG, H.; CHRITTON, D. B. et al. (1990b): The effects of moderate exercise training on natural killer cells and acute upper respiratory tract infections. In: *International Journal of Sports Medicine, 11,* 467–473.

NIEMAN, D. C.; NEHLSEN-CANARELLA, S. L.; FAGOAGA, O. R.; HENSON, D. A.; UTTER, A.; DAVIS, J. M. et al. (1998a): Influence of mode and action on the cytokine response to heavy exertion. In: *Medicine and Science in Sports and Exercise, 30,* 671–678.

NIEMAN, D. C.; NEHLSEN-CANARELLA, S. L.; FAGOAGA, O. R.; HENSON, D. A.; UTTER, A.; DAVIS, J. M. et al. (1998b): Effects of mode and carbohydrate on the granulocyte and monocyte response to intensive prolonged exercise. In: *Journal of Applied Physiology, 84,* 1252–1259.

NIEMAN, D. C.; PEDERSEN, B. K. (1999): Exercise and immune function: recent development. *Sports Medicine, 27,* 73–80.

ORTALDO, J. R.; GERARD, J. P.; HENDERSSON, L. E.; NEUBAU, R. H.; RABIN, H. (1983a): Responsiveness of purified natural killer cells to pure interleukin-2 (IL-2). In: OPPENHEIM, J.J.; RABIN, H.: *Interleukines, Lymphokines and Cytokines.* New York: Academic Press. 63–68.

ORTALDO, J. R.; MANTOVANI, A.; HOBBS, D.; RUBINSTEIN, M.; PESTKA, S.; HERBERMAN, R. B. (1983b): Effects of several species of human leukocyte interferon on cytotoxic activity of NK cells and monocytes. In: *International Journal of Cancer, 31,* 285–289.

ORTEGA, E.; COLLAZOS, M. E.; MAYNAR, M.; BARRIGA, C.; DE LA FUENTE, M. (1993): Stimulation of the phagocytic function of neutrophils in sedentary men after acute moderate exercise. In: *European Journal of Applied Physiology, 66,* 60–64.

OSHIDA, Y.; YAMANOUCHI, K.; HAYAMIZU, S.; SATO, Y. (1988): Effect of acute physical exercise on lymphocyte subpopulations in trained and untrained subjects. In: *International Journal of Sports Medicine, 9,* 137–140.

OSTROWSKI, K.; HERMANN, C.; BANGASH, A.; SCHJERLING, P.; NIELSEN, J. N.; PEDERSEN, B. K. (1998a): A trauma-like elevation in plasma cytokines in humans in response to treadmill running. In: *Journal of Physiology (London Then Cambridge), 508,* 949–953.

OSTROWSKI, K.; ROHDE, T.; ASP, S.; SCHJERLING, P.; PEDERSEN, B. K. (1999): The cytokine balance and strenuous exercise: TNF-alpha, IL-2beta, IL-6, IL-1ra, sTNF-r1, sTNF-r2, and IL-10. In: *Journal of Physio-*

logy (London Then Cambridge), 515, 287–291.

OSTROWSKI, K.; ROHDE, T.; ZACHO, M.; ASP, S.; PEDERSEN, B. K. (1998b): Evidence that IL-6 is produced in skeletal muscle during intense long-term muscle activity. In: Journal of Physiology (London Then Cambridge), 508, 949–953.

O'SHEA, J.; ORTALDO, J. R. (1992): The biology of natural killer cells: insights into the molecular basis of function. In: LEWIS, C. E.; McGEE, J. O.: The Natural Killer Cell. Oxford: Oxford University Press. 1–40.

PALMO, J.; ASP, S.; DAUGAARD, J. R.; RICHTER, E. A.; KLOKKER, M.; PEDERSEN, B. K. (1995): Effect of eccentric exercise on natural killer cell activity. In: Journal of Applied Physiology, 78, 1442–1446.

PAPA, S.; VITALE, M.; MAZZOTTI, G.; NERI, L. M.; MONTI, G.; MANZOLI, F. A. (1989): Impaired lymphocyte stimulation induced by long-term training. In: Immunology Letters, 22, 29–33.

PARRY BILLINGS, M.; BUDGETT, R.; KOUTE-DAKIS, Y.; BLOMSTRAND, E.; BROOKS, S.; WILLIAMS, C. et al. (1992): Plasma amino acid concentrations in the overtraining syndrome: possible effects on the immune system. In: Medicine and Science in Sports and Exercise, 24, 1353–1358.

PEDERSEN, B. K.; BRUUNSGAARD, H.; KLOKKER, M.; KAPPEL, M.; MACLEAN, D. A.; NIELSEN, H. B. et al. (1997): Exercise-induced immunomodulation - possible roles of neuroendocrine factors and metabolic factors. In: International Journal of Sports Medicine, 18, 2–7.

PEDERSEN, B. K.; CLEMMENSEN, I. H. (1997): Exercise and Cancer. In: PEDERSEN, B. K.: Exercise Immunology. Austin, Texas: R. G. Landes. 171-201.

PEDERSEN, B. K.; KAPPEL, M.; KLOKKER, M.; NIELSEN, H. B.; SECHER, N. H. (1994): The immune system during exposure to extreme physiologic conditions. In: International Journal of Sports Medicine, 15, 116–121.

PEDERSEN, B. K.; NIELSEN, H. B. (1997): Acute exercise and the immune system. In: Exercise Immunology. Edited by BK Pedersen.

PEDERSEN, B. K.; THOMSEN, B. S.; NIELSEN, H. (1986): Inhibition of natural killer cell activity by antigen-antibody complexes. In: Allergy, 41, 568–574.

PEDERSEN, B. K.; TVEDE, N.; CHRISTENSEN, L. D.; KLARLUND, K.; KRAGBAK, S.; HALKJR KRISTENSEN, J. (1989): Natural killer cell activity in peripheral blood of highly trained and untrained persons. In: International Journal of Sports Medicine, 10, 129–131.

PEDERSEN, B. K.; ULLUM, H. (1994): NK cell response to physical activity: possible mechanisms of action. In: Medicine and Science in Sports and Exercise, 26, 140–146.

PERSSON, S.; JONSDOTTIR, I.; THOREN, P.; POST, C.; NYBERG, F.; HOFFMANN, P. (1993): Cerebrospinal fluid dynorphin-converting enzyme activity is increased by voluntary exercise in the spontaneously hypertensive rat. In: Life Sciences, 53, 643–652.

PETERS, E. M.; BATEMAN, E. D. (1983): Ultramaraton running and upper respiratory tract infections. An epidemiological survey. In: South African Medical Journal, 64, 582–584.

PETERS, E. M.; CAMBELL, A.; PAWLEY, L. (1992): Vitamin A fails to increase resistance to upper respiratory in distance runners. In: South African Journal of Sports Medicine, 3–7.

PETERS, E. M.; GOETZSCHE, J. M.; GROBBELAAR, B.; NOAKES, T. D. (1993): Vitamin C supplementation reduces the incidence of postrace symptoms of upper-respiratory-tract infection in ultramarathon runners. In: American Journal of Clinical Nutrition, 57, 170–174.

PYNE, D. B. (1994): Regulation of neutrophil function during exercise. In: Sports Medicine, 17, 245–258.

PYNE, D. B.; GLEESON, M. (1997): Effects of intensive exercise training on immunity in athletes. In: International Journal of Sports Medicine, (In Press)

RIVIER, A.; PENE, J.; CHANEZ, P.; ANSELME, F.; CAILLAUD, C.; PREFAUT, C. et al. (1994): Release of cytokines by blood monocytes during strenuous exercise. In: *International Journal of Sports Medicine, 15,* 192–198.

ROHDE, T.; ASP, S.; MACLEAN, D. A.; PEDERSEN, B. K. (1998a): Competitive sustained exercise in humans, lymphokine activated killer cell activity, and glutamine - an intervention study. In: *European Journal of Applied Physiology, 78,* 448–453.

ROHDE, T.; MACLEAN, D.; PEDERSEN, B. K. (1998b): Effect of glutamine on changes in the immune system induced by repeated exercise. In: *Medicine and Science in Sports and Exercise, 30,* 856–862.

ROHDE, T.; MACLEAN, D. A.; HARTKOPP, A.; PEDERSEN, B. K. (1996): The immune system and serum glutamine during a triathlon. In: *European Journal of Applied Physiology, 74,* 428-434.

ROWBOTTOM, D. G.; KEAST, D.; GARCIA-WEBB, P.; MORTON, A. R. (1997): Training adaptation and biological changes among well-trained male triathletes. In: *Medicine and Science in Sports and Exercise, 29,* 1233–1239.

ROWBOTTOM, D. G.; KEAST, D.; MORTON, A. R. (1996): The emerging role of glutamine as an indicator of exercise stress and over-training. In: *Sports Medicine, 21,* 80–97.

SMITH, J. A. (1994): Neutrophils, host defense, and inflammation: a double-edged sword. In: *Journal of Leukocyte Biology, 56,* 672–686.

SMITH, J. A.; GRAY, A. B.; PYNE, D. B.; BAKER, M. S.; TELFORD, R. D.; WEIDEMAN, M. J. (1996): Moderate exercise triggers both priming and activation of neutrophil subpopulations. In: *American Journal of Physiology, 270,* 838–845.

SMITH, J. A.; MCKENZIE, S. J.; TELFORD, R. D.; WEIDEMANN, M. J. (1992): Why does moderate exercise enhance, but intense training depress, immunity? In: HUSBAND, A. J.: *Behaviour and Immunity.* Boca Raton: CRC-Press. 155–168.

SMITH, J. A.; TELFORD, R. D.; MASON, I. B.; WEIDEMANN, M. J. (1990): Exercise, Training and Neutrophil Microbicidal Activity. In: *International Journal of Sports Medicine, 11,* 179–187.

SPRENGER, H.; JACOBS, C.; NAIN, M.; GRESSNER, A. M.; PRINZ, H.; WESEMANN, W. et al. (1992): Enhanced release of cytokines, interleukin-2 receptors, and neopterin after long-distance running. In: *Clinical Immunology and Immunopathology, 63,* 188–195.

THARP, G. D.; BARNES, M. W. (1990): Reduction of saliva immunoglobulin levels by swim training. In: *European Journal of Applied Physiology, 60,* 61–64.

TOMASI, T. B.; TRUDEAU, F. B.; CZERWINSKI, D.; ERREDGE, S. (1982): Immune parameters in athletes before and after strenuous exercise. In: *Journal of Clinical Immunology, 2,* 173–178.

TONNESEN, E.; CHRISTENSEN, N. J.; BRINKLOV, M. M. (1987): Natural killer cell activity during cortisol and adrenaline infusion in healthy volunteers. In: *European Journal of Clinical Investigation, 17,* 497–503.

TVEDE, N.; HEILMANN, C.; HALKJAER KRISTENSEN, J.; PEDERSEN, B. K. (1989): Mechanisms of B-lymphocyte suppression induced by acute physical exercise. In: *Journal of Clinical Immunology, 30,* 169–173.

TVEDE, N.; KAPPEL, M.; KLARLUND, K.; DUHN, S.; HALKJAER KRISTENSEN, J.; KJAER, M. et al. (1994): Evidence that the effect of bicycle exercise on blood mononuclear cell proliferative responses and subsets is mediated by epinephrine. In: *International Journal of Sports Medicine, 15,* 100–104.

TVEDE, N.; STEENSBERG, J.; BASLUND, B.; HALKJAER KRISTENSEN, J.; PEDERSEN, B. K. (1991): Cellular immunity in highly trained elite racing cyclists during periods of training with high and low intensity. In: *Scandinavian Journal of Medicine and Science in Sports, 1,* 163–166.

ULLUM, H.; HAAHR, P. M.; DIAMANT, M.; PALMO, J.; HALKJAER KRISTENSEN, J.; PEDERSEN, B. K. (1994a): Bicycle exercise enhances plasma IL-6 but does not change IL-1alpha, IL-1beta, IL-6, or TNF-alpha pre-mRNA in BMNC. In: *Journal of Applied Physiology, 77,* 93–97.

ULLUM, H.; PALMO, J.; HALKJAER KRISTENSEN, J.; DIAMANT, M.; KLOKKER, M.; KRUUSE, A.

et al. (1994b): The effect of acute exercise on lymphocyte subsets, natural killer cells, proliferative responses, and cytokines in HIV-seropositive persons. In: *Journal of Acquired Immune Deficiency Syndromes, 7,* 1122–1133.

VANHELDER, W. P.; RADOMSKI, M. W.; GOODE, R. C. (1984): Growth hormone responses during intermittent weight lifting exercise in men. In: *European Journal of Applied Physiology, 53,* 31–34.

VENKATRAMAN, J. T.; PENDERGAST, D. (1998): Effect of the level of dietary fat intake and endurance exercise on plasma cytokines in runners. In: *Medicine and Science in Sports and Exercise, 30,* 1198–1204.

WEIDEMANN, M. J.; SMITH, J. A.; GRAY, A. B.; MCKENZIE, S. J.; PYNE, D. B.; KOLBUCH BRADDON, M. E. et al. (1992): Exercise and the immune system. In: *Today's Life Science, July,* 24–33.

WEINSTOCK, C.; KONIG, D.; HARNISCHERMACHER, R.; KEUL, J.; BERG, A.; NORTHOFF, H. (1997): Effect of exhaustive exercise stress on the cytokine response. In: *Medicine and Science in Sports and Exercise, 29,* 345–354.

WELSH, R. M.; VARGAS-CORTES (1992): Natural killer cells in viral infection. In: LEWIS, C. E.; MCGEE J. O.: *The Natural Killer Cell.* Oxford: Oxford University Press. 108–150.

Physical Activity and the Immune System

Wildor Hollmann / Heiko K. Strüder

Brain, Psyche, Mind, and Muscular Activity

1. Brain, mind, mood

At interdisciplinary congresses astrono-mers, physicists, biologists and medical doctors of various areas of expertise agree: the human brain represents the most complex and the least well resear-ched structure in the known universe. It does not only follow the usual laws of physics and chemistry, but also produces the "self-conscious mind", which can be defined as the ability for abstract thought under self-reflection, planning of the future and application of language. This aspect makes a qualitative diffe-rence between humans and animals. The "decade of brain research" – as it has been declared by the former American president BUSH in 1989/90 – has provided a huge amount of new know-ledge on the functioning of the human brain. For thousands of years, men have asked themselves where the mind origi-nates and how the flood of thoughts and ideas could be explained. "Mind" usually stands for the opposite of substance and body – the physical. In differentiation from the "soul", "mind" is characterized by the intellect, ability to think (reason) and includes consciousness. In this context, the term "mind" means the uniform connection of the psychic expe-riences of a human being.
In tradition with the many major thinkers of early history and the medieval period, DuBois-Reymond – one of the most important physiologists of his time – formulated in the year 1872: ["What a grateful connection exists between specific motions of specific atoms in my brain on the one hand and, on the other hand, the for me elementary, indefinable and undeniable facts: I feel pain, lust; I taste sweets, smell roses, listen to the sounds of the organ, see red or blue... It will always be incomprehensible that a number of carbon, nitrogen, oxygen atoms and so on is not indifferent about how they are lying and moving, how they stood and moved, how they will stand and will move. It is impossible to appre-hend, how consciousness can develop out of their interaction."]
The scientist, independent of the area of expertise, has to be primarily concerned with the knowledge of structure, physics and chemistry as well as their interaction on the basis of physiological processes. This knowledge can then be the founda-tion for the interpretation of the human mind.
A special phenomenon of our mind is the concept of *"time"*. Nowadays theories and formulas on the behavior of the physics world can practically say nothing on this matter. It is purely a phenomenon of the mind that can not be grasped with formulas of physics. HAWKING (1988) as well as PENROSE (1991) concluded that "space-time" is simply there, and that time – just like space itself – is not in progress. Only the mind requires a

flowing time. KORNHUBER (1973) recorded in volunteers electric signals from the brain by means of electrodes placed on the scalp. The temporal development of brain activity during voluntary work was measured. The subjects were requested to bend their index finger voluntarily at any chosen time-point. The result was: The electric potential builds up about 1–1.5s before the actual bending of the finger. However, the subjects were convinced that they had made the decision to bend the finger immediately before the bending and not about 1s before. The usual reaction time in case of external stimuli is only about $^1/_5$s. LIBET (1981, 1985, 1993) exposed patients who inevitably needed brain surgery to weak electric stimuli on specific brain areas or on the skin. The subjects became aware of both forms of stimuli only after at least $^1/_2$s. If the direct stimulation of the brain was carried out $^1/_2$s earlier than the stimulation of the skin, the subjects declared that they had felt the stimulation of the skin first. Thus, we subjectively compensate the always existing delay in time by means of a "back-dating". In case subjects were asked to voluntarily bend one finger and to mark the time-point of their decision with a stop-watch, about 0.2s went by between the electroencephalogram (EEG)-documented decision-making and its execution. The EEG showed neuronal activity already 0.3s before the manual stop of the watch. – In other words, the decision to move the finger was already made by the brain, before the mind realized it. The exact reasons for this phenomenon are not yet scientifically totally understood. ROTH (1994) considers the *mind to be a physics state*, just as electromagnetic waves, mechanics, heat or energy. The reason is: Thoughts, ideas – thus "mind" – can be visualized in different ways (e.g. by means of positron emission tomography (PET)). The mind can be influenced physiologically-pharmacologically, thus, it can be modified physiologically-chemically. Consequently, ROTH (1994) characterizes "voluntary motor function" as the kind of motor states which have their origin in a complex interaction between the associate cortical areas and subcortical centers. – This interpretation includes that the *states of the mind are subjectively experienced states resulting from specific processes in the brain, which the brain gives itself.*

Thus, according to ROTH one could *define the "I" as sensorimotor system and "mentality" in respect to the own body.* Sensorimotor system includes that the sensory organs provide information to the brain through differently firing neurons. However, this information does not form pictures but only local stimuli in the brain. "Mentality" includes that by means of comparison and combination of sensoric activities in connection with the respective memory the brain develops a "meaning" and evaluates it under brain-immanent criteria. The result has been named by ROTH *"constituents of reality, a construct by the brain".*

The general correctness of such considerations is underlined by findings from several brain researchers (CHURCHLAND, 1995; DAMASIO, 1997; BLACK, 1993; and so on). *Accordingly, "mind" would be a construct on the basis of a neuronal code plus experience plus current influence of the environment.*

In the "mind" *reason (ratio)* and *emotion (emotio)* are confronted with each others. In contrast to reason, however, emotions are less experienced in the brain but are rather localized in specific parts of the body. Happiness and excitement induce a "pounding heart", fear causes a "feeling of pressure in the stomach". From a biological viewpoint, it is well known that the main guiding principle is the promotion of the individual and the survival of the species. Feelings like thirst, hunger, but also the urge for urination and defecation serves for the survival of the individual. The compliance with these vital necessities, in the sense of for example drinking and eating, is "rewarded" by nature with positive feelings – so called *"reward centers"* in the brain are responsible for them. In neighboring areas in the brain, libido and the sexual intercourse serve in the same sense to ensure the survival of the species. To a certain extent it can be said that *nature uses tricks which serve to ensure the survival of the individual and the whole species.* The feeling of pain presents in this context a warning-signal. The origin of feeling is based on the stimulation of complexes of neurons, which are mainly located in the limbic system of the brain. It consists of nuclei and nerves, which are interlinked in many ways with the hypothalamus, brain-stem and especially with the cortex. The cortex itself shows a particularly strong developed frontal lobe, in which nerves out of many brain areas come together and from where projections to other regions are formed. *"Decisions"* are made in the same bundles of nerves which are also responsible for motor function. Therefore, "mind" in the sense of ratio and "feeling" in the sense of emotio as well as muscular motor function are superbly linked.

In 1931 the blood pressure reducing effect of rauwolfia serpentina was first discovered. 20 years later reserpine was isolated from this extract, the first substance in history which reduced high blood pressure. At the beginning of the 50^s we were very happy in the University Clinic of Cologne, as we were able to reduce blood pressure in hypertensives for the first time. Up to this date, blood letting had still occasionally been the applied method. Unfortunately, most of our patients returned to the hospital after several months and complained that they were constantly depressed. The degree of depression reached up to the point of being suicidal – which actually occurred several times worldwide. At that time we discontinued the therapy with this medication in those cases, without knowing the exact regulatory connections. Today it is known that reserpine causes a reduction of the three aminergic neurotransmitters (serotonin, dopamine, noradrenaline) in the brain. Reserpine simply depletes their vesicles in the synapsis. This induces a feeling of severe depression up to the threat of suicide.

"Mood" is the product of the quality and quantity of neurotransmitters or other chemical substances in the synapsis, especially in the area of the limbic system. This is true also for caffeine, cocoa and chocolate, alcohol and nicotine as well as for pharmacological substances, which directly affect the synapsis.

Following these basic considerations on ratio and emotio, it is intended in the next part of this paper to present our own experiments, which are partly related to this topic. These experiments were mainly done with STRÜDER (Institute of Theory of Training and Movement, DSHS); HERZOG (Research Center Jülich), HEISS and HERHOLZ (Max-Planck-Institute for Brain Research, and Institute for Neurology of the University of Cologne), DONIKE and SCHÄNZER (Institute for Biochemistry, DSHS) and PLATEN (Institute for Cardiology and Sports Medicine, DSHS) also contributed.

2. Regional blood flow and regional metabolism of the brain during ergometer exercise

Just a few years ago, the supply of blood to the human brain during muscular work was considered to be constant. The autonomous regulation of brain circulation was thought to be responsible for this. This view was first challenged by experiments from ROLAND and LARSEN (1976), who investigated voluntary movements of the hands. During rhythmic closing and opening of the hand, a significant increase in blood circulation was found on the opposite brain side in the area of the motor cortex responsible for the hand. Blood circulation was also augmented in neighboring areas of the body-sensation-sphere, because this is where sensory signals arrive. It was concluded from these and other findings that the areas of body-sensation-sphere and the motor cortex are organized as two bands which lie one behind the other reaching from one ear to the other crossing over the cerebral cortex.
Besides the motor, somatosensoric and associative areas voluntary muscular movements always activate the areas of the frontal lobes in both brain halves. Movements which are only imagined and

not executed also activate the respective motor area. In case of actual execution of the movement, the area of the hand and fingers in the motor cortex are also active. LASSEN et al. (1985) conclude from these results that the supplementary motor area is occupied with the programming of the movement, while the motor cortex is giving the actual orders for the movement and the body-sensation-sphere controls the execution of the orders. In addition to regional changes, *"remembering"* and *"thinking"* further increase the general blood circulation in the brain by about 10%. This effect does not occur if simple tasks are solved, however, it is particularly striking if the person is dealing with difficult problems (LASSEN et al., 1985).
As there have not yet been any studies applying reliable methods and investigating brain blood circulation during active work of large muscle groups, e.g. during cycle ergometry, we developed a special examination apparatus at the Max-Planck-Institute of Brain Research in Cologne. We then investigated the influence of cycle ergometry exertion of 25W as well as 100W on *regional blood flow* of the brain (HERHOLZ et al., 1987; HOLLMANN et al., 1994). Methodically, we made use of the ^{133}Xe bolus injection method. At a workload of only 25W, which corresponds approximately to the speed of slow walking, a significant increase in the regional blood circulation was found in 6 out of 8 examined areas of the cerebrum. The increase of the workload to 100W did not result in a linear increase of the blood flow, however, a highly significant increase was found in each individual brain area. These findings left no doubt that there is no autonomous center that ensures a

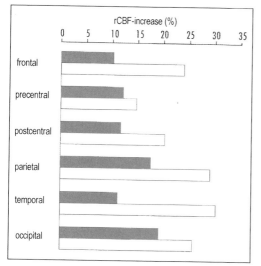

Fig. 1: Increase (%) of blood flow during cycle ergometry at 25 watts (black bars) and 100 watts (white bars) in different regions of the brain. o = basal value (HERHOLZ et al., 1987).

constant blood flow in the human brain during muscular work (Fig. 1).
Up to now, the causes for the increased blood flow remain unknown. There are some indications pointing to an involvement of proprioceptors in tendons and muscles, as only dynamic work – movements – but not heavy static work induces an increase of blood flow in the brain.
The causes for the regional augmentations of blood circulation during muscular work are also unknown. The mechanisms responsible for an increase in blood circulation in the brain at rest do not apply during muscular work. At rest, the strongest stimulus for an increase in brain blood flow is the increase of the CO_2 partial pressure in the arterial blood. However, during exercise the CO_2 partial pressure is known to decline in the arterial blood (HOLLMANN, 1963). In addition,

a reduction of oxygen saturation in the arterial blood is not found during light and medium muscular demands. An augmentation in the metabolism of the respective brain areas is unlikely due to the fact that the sum of electric activities hardly changes at all in comparison to rest. The increase in blood pressure during moderate work is so small, that an effect on the regional blood circulation should not occur. It is also unlikely that the decline of the pH-value is the cause, especially, because the increments in lactate concentration are only marginal. There is also almost no change in ammonia concentration. It is possible, albeit speculative, that an increased release of potassium ions in the areas of neuronal capillaries induces a dilatation of the arterioles.
At rest, brain cells almost exclusively use carbohydrates as energy substrates for their metabolism. Thus in further studies of our own at the Nuclear Research Center in Jülich, glucose metabolism during cycle ergometry was investigated applying the PET method and the [18]fluorodeoxiglucose-marker. After a 10-min period in order to reach the steady-state at a work load of 60% of the individual maximum performance capacity, we registered in the subjects under these standardized aerobic conditions the regional glucose metabolism in the brain. Surprisingly, a decline by 4–19%, in the cerebellum by 6%, was found. As the only exception, an increase of glucose metabolism by about 9% was detected in the occipital cortex (Fig. 2). From the findings it can be concluded that the described blood flow increase in regional areas of the brain during muscular work cannot be attributed to an intensification of glucose metabolism

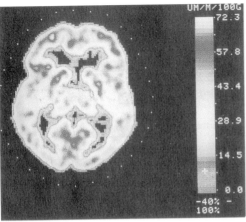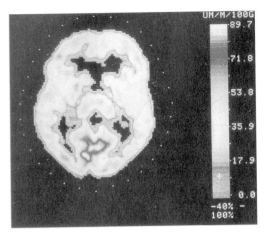

Fig. 2: Extent of glucose metabolism in regional areas of the brain during cycle ergometry at 60% of the individual maximal oxygen uptake (after 10 min of exercise). The darker the spots, the higher the carbohydrate metabolism at this area. In comparison to rest, during exercise far less dark spots are found in the frontal and parietal area, while increments were registered in the occipital area (HERZOG et al., 1992).

(HERZOG et al., 1992; HOLLMANN et al., 1996). Based on further studies, we now assume that a compensatory metabolisation of keton bodies occurs in the areas of the brain which show a reduction of glucose metabolism during muscular work.

3. Endogenous opioid peptides and pain sensitivity during muscular work

We hypothesized that the reason for the regional increase in blood flow during muscular work mentioned above might be to ensure that substances which are increasingly released during exercise can be transported as compactly and quickly as possible to the intended destination. In order to prove this theory, we first carried out studies on endogenous opioids. In 1975, HUGHES et al. discovered these CNS-inherent morphine derivatives. To date, 52 different opioid peptides have been determined. Besides numerous psychic and physical factors, muscular exercise may cause an increase in these substances in the blood. The higher the physical work load, the greater the rise. As a prerequisite for such an increase, either the load intensity must be so high that, for example, a lactate level of 4mmol/l in the arterial blood is surpassed, or the demand must last longer than about 60min, or a threshold for the psychic demand must be exceeded. The higher plasma level of opioid peptides during greater exertion may contribute to the fact that top level athletes in the relevant sports (e. g., 400-m run, rowing) tolerate high lactate acidosis relatively well. Additionally, it can be speculated that the high lactate level during training of wrestlers and weight-lifters can be endured better due to the simultaneously high endorphin production.

In double blind experiments, we were able to prove that *pain sensitivity* as well as *pain tolerance* can be highly significantly changed using naloxon as an opioid blocker. By means of an especially designed crown placed on a tooth and connected with an electric contact to the dental pulp, we investigated the pain sensitivity and pain tolerance in 10 subjects immediately following a cycle ergometry to exhaustion. After exercise, the threshold for both pain sensitivity and pain tolerance was significantly increased. In the following trial, subjects received either saline or naloxon. After application of the opioid-blocker naloxon, subjects were significantly more pain sensitive – even after exercise – compared to normal conditions at rest. During the placebo trial subjects reported an improvement of mood after exercise, whereas after naloxon, psychological questionnaires revealed that the mood was very bad and aggressive (ARENTZ et al., 1986) (Fig. 3).

Opioid receptors are distributed in a typical pattern in the brain. The medium part of the thalamus is an area with a high density. The thalamus is the main entrance to the brain and filters incoming sensoric information as well as forwards it to the cerebral cortex. In addition, a particular high density of opioid receptors is located in the limbic system. From there nerve tractus aim into e.g. the hypothalamus, which controls the pituitary gland and thus affects the entire hormonal situation of the body. This makes it understandable that the emotional situations reflect themselves in the hormonal profile in the whole body. *"Starting fever"* and *"pre-start tension"* of the athlete present a psychic modulation of the state of the body. This is where the connections between thought processes and "autonomous" reactions such as, for example, the heart rate are modulated. The locus coeruleus also sends neuronal projections to the limbic system and contains opioid receptors. It functions with the neurotransmitter noradrenaline and can be influenced by opioids through this mechanism.

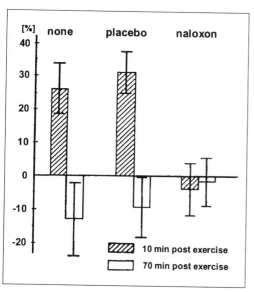

Fig. 3: Pain sensation (%) following cycle ergometry to exhaustion (double blind experiment; n = 10). "none" = pre examination, "placebo" = saline, "naloxon" = opioid antagonist. After blockade of the endogenous opioids (endorphines), the pain sensitivity is higher than under basal conditions at rest (ARENTZ et al., 1986).

4. Effects of neurotransmitter agonists and antagonists

We investigated the specific function of serotonin and dopamine in combination with cycle ergometry. For the studies on

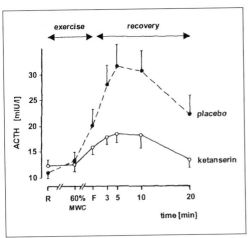

Fig. 4: The serotonin antagonist ketanserin reduces the usual physiological increase in ACTH during maximal physical work (placebo). Up to an intensity of 60% of the maximal oxygen uptake no significant differences were found between trials (DE MEIRLEIR et al., 1985d).

serotonin, we administered healthy male subjects the *serotonin antagonist* ketanserin. The maximal oxygen uptake as well as the heart rate at rest and during exercise were not affected by ketanserin, however, a reduction in systolic blood pressure was found during exercise. On work load levels below 60% of the individual maximal oxygen uptake ketanserin showed no effect on prolactin release. An increase above 60% of the maximal oxygen uptake significantly reduced exercise-induced prolactin increments. Ketanserin application also led to significant lower ACTH and TSH concentrations in the plasma during exercise to exhaustion (DE MEIRLEIR et al., 1985d) (Fig. 4). Using the *dopamine agonist* pergolide, we investigated the effect of *dopamine* during muscular work on the cycle ergometer. The exercise-induced increase in prolactin was totally abolished by admi-

nistration of pergolide. At the same time, significant higher LH concentrations were found in comparison to the placebo trial. Also, the usual ACTH increments during muscular work were suppressed by pergolide. Heart rate and systolic blood pressure were reduced during exercise. Maximal oxygen uptake as the gross criteria of the cardio-pulmonary-metabolic capacity was significantly increased, while the capillary lactate concentrations were reduced on given

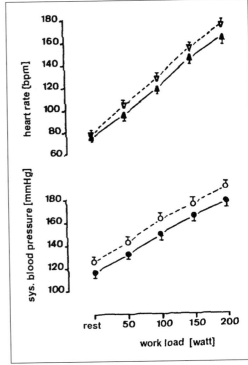

Fig. 5: Artificial increase of the effects induced by dopamine (pergolide, closed symboles) causes a significant augmentation of the performance capacity of the heart, cardiovascular and pulmonary system as well as metabolism. On given work load levels (watt) a reduction of the heart rate (top) and the systolic blood pressure (bottom) was found (n = 10) (DE MEIRLEIR et al., 1987a).

Brain, Psyche, Mind, and Muscular Activit

work loads (De Meirleir et al., 1987a) (Fig. 5).

In another study, we addressed the question of whether the artificial *alteration of serotonin concentration in the synoptic cleft* modifies physical performance capacity. In a double blind study, we used the substance paroxetine, which inhibits the reuptake of serotonin after release into the synaptic cleft after chronic application. The result was a highly significant reduction of endurance capacity (Fig. 6). It seems likely that through this drug the motivation is negatively influenced and the subjects feel that they can no longer continue to exercise, despite the fact that all the other performance-relevant parameters do not show any difference to the placebo trial (Strüder et al., 1998a).

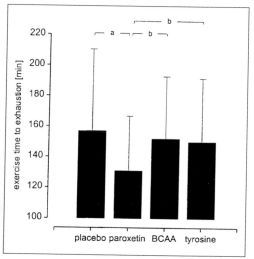

Fig. 6: Exercise time to exhaustion during test units with placebo, paroxetine (serotonin reuptake inhibitor), branched-chain amino acids (BCAA) and tyrosine (dopamine precursor) administration. Significance level (ANOVA, Newman-Keuls) was set at p < 0.05 (b) and p < 0.01 (a) (Strüder et al., 1998a).

5. Hypoxia, hyperoxia, and neurotransmitter regulation during exercise

Variation of the O_2 partial pressure in the inspired air induces changes in central steering mechanisms during physical work of different intensities. Hypoxia modifies for example the function of the blood-brain barrier (Lataste, 1992). An increase of the brain blood flow, a vasodilatation of the brain capillaries and an augmentation of the brain capillary pressure has been proven. Thus, we investigated the effect of changes in O_2 partial pressure on the well established hormonal and neurotransmitter responses during exercise.

In three trials, healthy male subjects were exposed to either normoxic (21% O_2), hyperoxic (100% O_2) or hypoxic (14% O_2 in 86% N_2) air for 30 min before exercise, during exercise over 60 min as well as 30 min post exercise. Heart rate, lactate and perceived exertion showed a significantly higher increase under hypoxia compared with normoxia and hyperoxia. Under hypoxia and normoxia no significant changes were found at rest before exercise in the concentrations of the catecholamines as well as of testosterone, growth hormone (STH) and ACTH (Fig. 7 and 8).

Under hyperoxia, noradrenaline and adrenaline declined slightly during this time period. During exercise, increments of adrenaline, noradrenaline, testosterone, STH and ACTH were found in all trials. Testosterone concentrations did not differ between trials. Hyperoxia induced an *extreme increase in the prolactin* concentration (400%) even before exercise was begun. During exercise, prolactin concentrations declined slightly (Fig. 8).

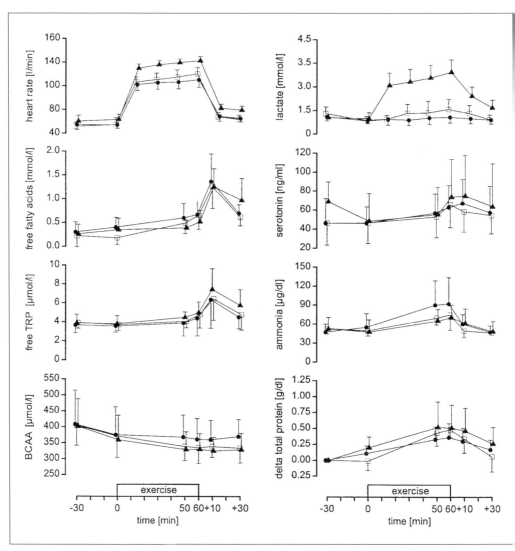

Fig. 7: Heart rate, concentrations of free fatty acids, free tryptophan, branched-chain amino acids (BCAA), lactate, serotonin, ammonia and delta total protein at different times before, during and after cycle ergometry in trials during hyperoxia (100% O_2, circles), hypoxia (14% O_2, 86% N_2, triangles) and normoxia (squares) (STRÜDER et al., 1996a).

In further prolactin-related studies we found during gradual increase of the O_2 partial pressure in the inspired air an insensitivity of the prolactin response up to a concentration of 40% O_2 which means a doubling of the normal O_2 partial pressure (STRÜDER et al., 1999b). Oxygen increments above 40% induced prolactin augmentations which reached the maximal values at a concentration of

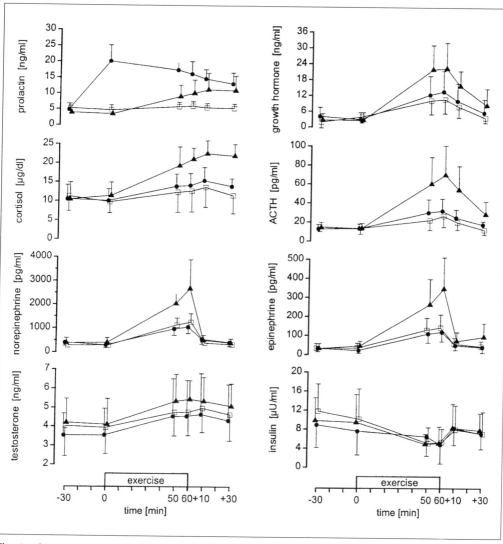

Fig. 8: Concentrations of plasma prolactin, cortisol, noradrenalin, testosterone, growth hormone, adrenocorticotropic hormone (ACTH), adrenalin and insulin at different times in the three trials. For further explanations see Fig. 7 (STRÜDER et al., 1996a).

100% O₂ in the inspired air (Fig. 9). Due to the fact that these high oxygen concentrations may have toxic effects if inspired for longer than three hours, *prolactin might present a stress response* which has not yet been known in this respect (HOLLMANN, unpublished). It can be speculated that the biochemical cause of the prolactin release is the reduction of the inhibitory effect of the dopminergic system or oxygen-induced changes in the synthesis of serotonin.

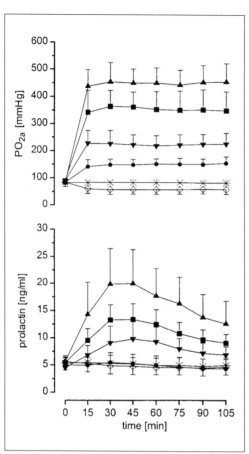

with intensities ranging from 50–70% of the maximal oxygen uptake. This is particularly the case if intramuscular glycogen resources have been reduced by exercise. Free tryptophan is the precursor of serotonin, tyrosin that of dopamine, adrenaline and noradrenaline. Neither of these amino acids can be synthesized in the brain but must be assimilated via the blood-brain barrier out of the plasma pool. There are at least three different carrier systems at the blood-brain barrier. The transport of the branched-chain amino acids (BCAA) and aromatic amino acids takes place competitively at the carrier for large neutral amino acids (LNAA).

The transport rate of aromatic and branched-chain amino acids is determined by their peripheral plasma levels. During endurance exercise, *BCAA* are taken up into the muscle and the liver to a larger extent than tryptophan. Consequently, the concentration of these amino acids declines in the plasma. Thus, the probability arises that tryptophan can occupy a carrier at the blood-brain barrier. The result is an increased admission of tryptophan into the brain, with subsequent transformation into serotonin, since the enzyme tryptophanhydroxylase is not saturated with tryptophan (CHAOULOFF, 1989).

Fig. 9: Blood oxygen partial pressures (pO_{2a}) and plasma prolactin concentrations in trials under 105 min of inhalation of gas containing oxygen fractions of 14% (open squares), 21% (stars), 40% (circles), 60% (inverted triangles), 80% (squares) and 100% (triangles) (STRÜDER et al., 1999b).

6. Changes of amino acid transport across the blood-brain barrier during physical work

Protein oxidation may cover 3–15% of the total energy metabolism during muscular work characterized by general aerobic dynamic endurance demands

In our studies, the artificial and exercise-induced increase of free fatty acids resulted in highly significant increments of plasma *free tryptophan* and the ratio of free tryptophan/LNAA (FISCHER et al., 1991; STRÜDER et al., 1996c, 1997, 1998a, 1999a) (Fig. 10). Increasing free fatty acids in nonphysiological areas by infusions during exercise led to no further increase of the ratio of free tryptophan/total tryptophan.

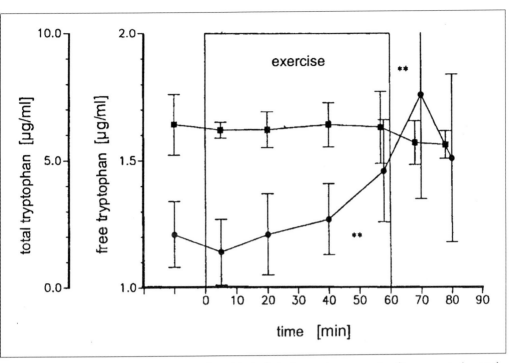

Fig. 10: *Increase of plasma free tryptophan (circles) during cycle ergometry* (FISCHER *et al.*, 1991).

We considered *ammonia* as a possible further influential substance affecting *serotonin synthesis* in the brain during exercise. During intensive exertion, the ammonia values significantly rise in the blood. This may affect serotonin synthesis in the brain or the transport mechanisms at the L-Carrier, respectively, in reference to an increase of the transport of LNAA into the brain (MANS et al., 1983; CARDELLY-CANGIANO et al., 1984). The augmentation of ammonia induces an increase of glutamine (GLN) in the brain and, thus, also leads to an increased transport of GLN over the L-Carrier out of the brain. Under assistance of glia cells and endothelium, in hyper-ammonia, GLN is increasingly transported out of the brain, and the intake of LNAA is promoted. Therefore, the hypothetical possibility exists that the exercise-induced rise of tryptophan in the brain as well as the augmented prolactin release during endurance exercise is not only influenced by the peripheral increase in free tryptophan. Additionally, the amount of amino acids – and thereby also of free tryptophan – transported into the brain could be raised by the intensified transport activity of the carriers for large neutral amino acids.

As it is well-established that serotonin has an inhibitory effect on *food intake*, we investigated the serum concentrations of the serotonin precursor tryptophan and the concentrations of LNAA in *anorexic female runners*. Treadmill running at 60% of the maximal oxygen uptake for two hours induced in anorexic runners a nonsignificant increase of tryptophan in comparison to a significant decline of tryptophan in non-anorexic runners.

It can be concluded from these results that in anorexic female runners modifications of serotonergic brain functions might be connected with food intake habits and magnitudes of caloric intake (PLATEN et al., 1993).

7. Psychic effects during physical work

Almost totally independent of the kind of sports, everyone who exercises has experienced feeling more relaxed and in a positive mood following these physical demands. Everyday problems appear to be smaller during the first hours post exercise. KNIPPING, director of the Medical University Clinic in Cologne, already mentioned this effect of physical work in a lecture in the year of 1949, and concluded that unknown biochemical mechanisms influence our brain.

As the cause for these improvements in mood, which have been objectively assessed by means of psychological questionnaires (NITSCH, 1976), several mechanisms are possible. We already mentioned the decrease of glucose metabolism in neurons during physical exercise and the possible compensation by metabolisation of *keton bodies*. This could come along with an improvement in mood. In ages past, the teleological meaning could have been to counterbalance the physical pain during a long lasting fight or attack by an opponent and, thus, be able to endure the physical demand for a longer period.

Another possible mechanism for the better mood might be the release of *endorphines* under the conditions mentioned above. The high density of opioid receptors in the limbic system point in this direction. Also, in the studies described above we were able to objectively demonstrate that "endorphine-increments" improve mood.

A third possibility for the improvement in mood could be augmented synthesis of *serotonin* or *dopamine* in the brain. A higher amount of serotonin in the limbic system improves the mood while a decrease of serotonin below a critical threshold promotes the development of depression, which may even result into suicide. The increase in synthesis of serotonin is based on the augmented entrance of tryptophan into the brain. Two regulatory mechanisms are involved: During long lasting physical work, we found an increased *change from albumin-bound tryptophan to free tryptophan* (FISCHER et al., 1991). This increases the probability that free tryptophan can occupy a carrier for transport over the blood-brain barrier and, therefore, also augments serotonin synthesis. The second possibility to raise brain tryptophan content during endurance exercise is the *decline of branched-chain amino acids,* which – as already mentioned – are particularly taken up by muscle and liver cells in case of depleted glycogen stores. Again, this decreases for free tryptophan the competition at the L-carrier of the blood-brain barrier. Finally, it should be mentioned that the decrease of plasma *insulin* concentration during long lasting physical exercise is reversed post exercise. One function of insulin is to increase the entrance of BCAA into the muscle cells. This also initiates the mechanism at the blood-brain barrier described above.

Besides physical exercise, mood can also be influenced by intake of foodstuffs and stimulants. *Caffeine* induces its stimulating effect by occupying the binding sides of the brain-immanent transmitter adenosin. This may for example block noradrenergic synapsis. The effect decreases with time due to habituation. *Cocoa* and *chocolate* contain theobromine and phenylethylamine. The latter is similar in its effect to amphetamines. Thus, these substances may also induce for example reactions of the heart (heart palpitation).

Alcohol induces in increase of endorphins. The production of the biogenic amino acid derivatives tetrahydrocaroline and tetrahydropapaveroline is simultaneously increased. Depending on the dosis, these substances may improve mood, take away inhibitions and augment sexual desire.

The findings mentioned above point to an intensive connection between functions of the brain, the cardio-circulatory system and the skeletal muscles on a biochemical basis.

8. Molecular-biological findings

A synapsis is an extremely dynamic unit, which can change from one millisecond to the other and store information simultaneously. The respective findings were discovered on a scientific basis less than two decades ago. Only recently it could be proven that neurotransmitters and nerve growth factors occur together in neurons. In response to stimuli from the environment or from the cerebral cortex itself *(thoughts)*, chemical circuits are built, dissolved and rebuilt again within a single neuroanatomic linking (BLACK, 1993). The approximately 10^{15} synapses in the brain make communication a key issue. *Thus, the biochemistry of communication and the "symbole-function" is crucial for the understanding of the function of the brain and the mind.* The expression of specific genes changes constantly, with the result that different kinds of gene products are built, which are important for the flow of information in the nervous system. E. g., genes which are responsible for the synthesis of neurotransmitters underlie a complex regulation by the environment (BLACK et al., 1987). The fact that each single neuron contains several different transmitters leads to an immense combined potential. The structure of the synaptic apparatus is also affected by *changes in the environment*. Specific experiences change the molecular structure of synapses (WU, BLACK, 1989). Even the morphology and amount can be modified by this (GREENOUGHT, 1984). For example, the simultaneous electric activation of different nerve-fibres in rats leads to a strengthening of synapses in the hippocampus. Such a synaptic strengthening is called longterm potentiation (LTP). It appears that an increase in the number of synapses and changes in the structure of each individual synapse comes along with these changes (LYNCH, 1986). The neurotransmitter glutamate seems to initiate this process by means of interactions with specific receptors in neurons of the hippocampus (NICOLL 1988). Therefore, a neurotransmitter has two functions in this case: they forward stimulating information within milliseconds and additionally promote the growth of synapses – this affects the achitecture of the whole circuit.

Rats which are living in an environment with diverse stimuli show in their cerebral cortex a significantly higher number of synapses than control rats which are only exposed to few stimuli. The number of synapses per neuron increases just as do the density of synapses and the length of the dentric spines (BLACK, 1993).

One of the most astonishing processes is the regulation of the neuronal function by the environment on a *genetic level. Through the neuronal impulse-activity, the environment thus has influence on the genome and, therefore, also on the plan for the neuronal structure and function* (BLACK, 1993). This dynamic presents the central mechanism of information processing. It is the communication through the activity of transmitters, tropic and growth factors, which mediates the constant neuronal reorganization.

The immense variety of mental possibilities based on the plasticity of the brain becomes obvious from this consideration: if a nerve cell, for example, expresses four different transmitters, which depending on the environment might occur independently of each other in three different concentrations, it would result in 81 (3^4) theoretically possible different transmitter constellations in this one single neuron. The human brain contains about 100 billion neurons, of which each single one might occur in some hundred different transmitter states. This results in an incredible potential for reception and memory of information.

Additionally, these circuits are electrically coded (BARTFAI et al., 1986). Electric

impulses with different rates and patterns initiate in particular neurons the release of specific combinations of transmitters. Changes due to stimuli from the environment, which have only occurred for seconds up to minutes, can remain for days and weeks (ZIGMOND et al., 1989). This makes it understandable that even simple systems of neuron contain a certain form of memory – the amplification of information from the environment. *Therefore, on a molecular level the memory is spread over the whole nervous system, and not only located in one single area of the brain.*

On the contrary, long-term memories (which can be kept for decades or even a whole life), by means of transmitter changes, might be based on increased synthesis of messenger-RNS as expression of an influence on the neuronal genome (BIGUET et al., 1986).

The "locations" of neuronal communication in the synapsis are transmitters, receptors and ion channels. The *catecholaminergic synapses have played a key role* in the development of the knowledge we have nowadays (BLACK, 1993). The *nerve growth factor (NGF)* supports the survival, development and function of neurons of the sympathetic and central nervous system. *Tyrosinhydroxylase (TH)* is the rate limiting enzyme in the biosynthesis of the catecholamines. It transfers tyrosine into L-dopa so that other steps can follow. An increased impulse rate stimulates the synthesis of transmitters in dopaminergic, noradrenergic and adrenergic neurons. Below a rate of about five stimuli per second (5 Hz), small changes in the impulse rate induce high changes in the amount of transmitters which are released (MELANDER, 1960). The responding receptors are not only found on the post-synaptic membrane but are also located presynaptically. Activation of these receptors modifies the release of the transmitters out of the presynaptic neuron. This method allows the neuron to control its own activity and regulate the release of the neurotransmitters through a negative feedback mechanism. The *postsynaptic thickening (PSD)* is a structure which might play an important role in the change from molecular mechanisms into long lasting morphological-functional modifications. It is subject to longterm changes associated with learning and memory. A PSD contains a group of filament proteins which are mobile and give shape. Therefore, it might be possible for PSD to undergo dynamic changes in their architecture. The normal neuronal activity thus induces molecular changes, which then modify structure and function of the synapses. Entering calcium ions activate the calcium-calmodulin-kinases, which again have an impact on the proteins of the PSD.

The change of the *spines* shape seems to also affect their electric characteristics. A series of molecular reactions can modify the morphology of the dentric spines so that the synapses are strengthened permanently. This could, for example, be one step in the process of building memory in the hippocampus.

The TH-induction in synaptic neurons is inhibited by an increased impulse activity of inhibitors of the protein and RNS-synthese (MÜLLER et al., 1969). Muscular exercise or stress, such as cold temperature increase the flux of sympathetic stimuli to the adrenal gland. Subsequently, increments of the presynaptic release of acetylcholine, the postsynaptic depolarisation and the simultaneous influx of sodium induce an increase in the number of TH-molecules in the postsynaptic nerve cell. Consequently, the synthesis of catecholamines is also augmented.

This allows for a *transferal of short processes into longterm changes.* The effect of repeated stimuli is much larger than the effect of one stimuli. The half-life after the induction is about two days. The amount of TH almost returned to the basal value by one week after the initial stimuli (THOENEN et al., 1970). Therefore, it seems that TH plays an important role during the "fight of flight response" as decisive regulator of the sympathetic-adrenal axis. The whole process is initiated by stimuli from the environ-ment. All connected later changes of the cardio-pulmonary-metabolic system have the activation of the adrenals as a prerequisite.

The electric neuronal stimulation rate regulates the chemical nature of the released transmitters. The transmitter-peptide-neurons usually secrete their peptide at a higher impulse rate than the one necessary for the classical trans-mitter alone. This is why a neuron can function at a very low stimulation rate (below 2 Hz) as a classical transmitter-releasing cell and at a very high impulse rate exclusively as a peptide cell. In case of medium rates totally different amounts of both substances can be released (BARFAI et al., 1986). The impor-tance of this finding is: stimuli from the environment might change the rate-pattern of the impulses and thereby indi-rectly influence the form of the bioche-mical message of the neuron – thus, also the nature of the respective information (BLACK, 1993).

The mechanism becomes even more complicated if it is taken into consideration that co-transmitters in a cell influence each other. E.g., acetylcholine inhibits the release of peptides by binding to specific presynaptic autoreceptors. On the other hand, a peptide may also reduce the release of acetylcholine by binding to neuronal peptide-receptors. The storage of the different transmitters of one neuron in totally separated vesicles makes communication easier (BROWNSTEIN, MEZEY, 1986).

Neurons of the sympathetic nervous system contain for example encephaline, adenosin, neuropeptide Y, cholecystokinin, releasing factor of the luteinising hormone (LHRH) and the vasoactive intestinal peptide (VIP) (HANLEY, 1989). *Thus, each state of the neurotransmitters has its specific functions, e. g., for the cardio-circulatory, pulmonary, digestive and urogenital system.*

In this context, the nerve growth factor (NGF) is of special importance. The nerve cells of the brain – which are built in large surplus – lose from the embrionic to the fully developed state about 40% of the total number of neurons (COWAN et al., 1984). However, animals treated with the nerve growth factor (NGF) showed a strikingly increased "survival-rate" of sensoric as well as sympathetic nerve cells (SUTTER et al., 1984). Several detailed studies have shown that the competition of the individual neurons for receiving the nerve growth factor decides which cells will survive. Additionally, it appears that the NGF also dynamically regulates the function of the system. NGF increases the amount of transmitters in neurons and, thereby, also the transmission of the signals. In respect to the NGF, built in the "destina-tion-area", competition exists between the sympathetic and sensoric neurons. The number of surviving neurons, the relative size of the surplying neurons and the pattern of the connection depends on this competition (KESSLER et al., 1983). *The innervating neurons require NGF throughout their lives.* Therefore, the competition also takes place the entire time, and a new regulation of the supply of the nerve is always possible (BLACK, 1993).

Movements in the sense of activity of the skeletal muscle influence the response of neurons in the hippocampus. It appears that the hippocampus encodes the spatial context in the outside world under consideration of experience in connection with motor activity of the organism (EICHENBAUM et al., 1989). The interaction between physical activity, stimuli from the environment and the plasticity of the brain down to the molecular level does not leave any doubt that the traditional differentiation between trophic factors, growth factors and transmitters is outdated (BLACK, 1993). E. g., the classical transmitters serotonin and acetylcholin influence the growing process of neurits. Insulin and the insulin-like growth factors have functions of transmitters and also regulate the development of neurits as well as the segmentation activity of neurons.

The human *mind in the sense of the sum of ratio and emotio* is able to initiate an abundance of hormonal reactions. Additionally, neurotransmitters themselves can modify existing hormonal reactions in qualitatively and quantitatively goal-oriented graduation. In one of our studies, for example, we did not only find a suppression of the ACTH and prolactin increments after application of a substance with dopamin agonistic properties, but also a highly significant increase of growth hormone (STH), which exceeded up to 100% above the normal exercise-induced augmentation (DE MEIRLEIR et al., 1987a).

Also, the thoughts and feelings may affect the *immune system* within seconds. The lymphocyte is the most important cellular factor of the immune response. On its membranes, the lymphocyte contains a large amount of different receptors, which may also offer neurotransmitters and hormones places to attach (UHLENBRUCK, ORDER, 1987). The immunological responses induced by this may take effect in form of a strengthening or weakening of the defense. The resulting hormonal response simultaneously induces a feed-back to the neurons of the brain. Posi-tive, happy thoughts strengthen the immune system; negative ideas, grief, sorrow or a so-called negative basic atti-tude weaken the immune system. This explains findings from epidemiological studies, which, for example, have shown an increased risk for cancer in depressive patients, while persons with a positive and happy attitude are less likely to develop cancer.

9. Network brain, network human being

Some brain researchers during the last decades were convinced that the geno-type is almost the only decisive factor for the wiring (considered as permanent) between the neurons in the brain. This belief has now been disproven. The human genome consists of about 3 billion pairs of bases. One out of four bases can be docked to each place of the genome, consequently, each place contains information of two bits resulting in a total information capacity of the human genome of six billion bits. As indi-cation for the quantity of information in the field of computers, eight bits equal one byte. Therefore, the content of infor-mation in the human genotype amounts to 6/8 billion byte equaling 750 mega-bytes (SPITZER, 1998).

A common CD of 12cm in diameter contains information in an amount of 680 megabytes (SCHLICHT, 1995). Thus, the nucleus of each cell of the human body contains information in an amount of approximately one CD. However, the 750 megabytes in the genotype are opposed by 1.25 billion megabytes, which are required by the brain only for the coding of its connections (SPITZER, 1998). This means: if the total amount of information of the human cells would only be used for the coding of linkings, the capacity would be totally insufficient for a genetic determination. The required amount of information is greater by the factor 10^3 to 10^8 (or even more) than the total capacity that is at disposal. Thus, the human brain cannot contain a permanent wiring; human beings learn in their brains domi-nantly by experience (SPITZER, 1998). The "trick of nature" consists in the construction of neuronal networks as information-processing systems. Its flexibility is based on the immense number of simple circuits. Apart from the biological facts, the function of a neuron lies in the creation of mathematical products (input times weight of the synapse), the summation of these products and the comparison of this sum with a threshold-value. The work of the calculation is distributed over all neurons and takes place simultaneously – that is why it has been called parallel information-processing (SPITZER, 1998). Like everywhere else in nature, with increasing knowledge about the function of the human brain, the view of a dynamic rather than static element has become prominent. Some researchers even speak of a neodarwinistic principle in the development of the human brain and its mind (CALVIN, 1990).

The close connection between environment and functions of the brain – also within neuronal nets – has been shown in experiments with rats. As an effect of learning, neurons can be found in the hippocampus, the organisator of the long-term memory, which are only active if the animal is located in a specific place (so-called "location-cells"). 20–30% of the neurons have been found to be such location-cells. They always fire particularly strongly, if the rat is at a certain location. By means of the calculation of the vectors of all location-cells it has been possible to find out at what place the rat had been under specific conditions of the cage. A period of 11–20 min was sufficient to increase the number of cells which are responsible for the coding of the location. In case of a new location, neurons which did not show any spatial preference before had learned the new area of the cage after only 10 min. Stable representations of the room were formed in the animal's hippocampus. Nevertheless, the old knowledge had still not been forgotten (WILSON, MCNAUGHTON, 1993).

There are surprising distributions of responsibilities in the neuronal nets. The human brain only consists of 0.1% of neurons, which are directly active in a sensory or motoric manner (NAUTA, FEIRTAG, 1990). Thus, 99.9% of the cortical neurons receive their input from other cortical neurons and also project their output to other cortical neurons. It could be formulated: *The brain is mainly concerned with itself.*

The conclusion out of all of these findings is that at an early age, children's brains should be exposed to as many motoric and sensoric stimuli as possible. Particularly by means of physical activity, additional synapses could be built and, therefore, isolated neurons and the connected degeneration could be prevented. Theoretically, the increasing existence of neurons and their respective synapsis should provide a better basis for the development of *intelligence,* which means according to our definition the ability of analysis, synthesis, memory as well as for originality. However, negative sides of this possibility should also be considered. For example, if a child sees violence and horror on TV several times a day, as a neuronal adaptation violence will inevitably be given less importance and will be considered to be a "normal" part of our everyday lives.

The age-related reduction of dendrites and particularly of spines impairs the short-term memory. In this respect, the findings mentioned above might be encouraging, as intensified physical and intellectual demands might not only oppose this degeneration in a structural and functional way, but possibly also – in case of appropriate motor function and the accompanying increase in regional blood flow and release of nerve growth factors – rebuild spines (ECCLES, 1993).

10. Hypothesis for the origin of thoughts and their psychosomatic consequences

Chaotic oszillations of different cell associations exist in the cerebrum. They are based on energy supported exchange processes of ions through neuronal membranes, especially of microtubuli. A signal from one or from several of the five sensory organs and/or from the brain itself induces a uniform alignment of the oscillations in special areas in the prefrontal cortex – it is the origin of thought (Fig. 11). According to this, a thought would be identical with the mentioned processes of exchanging ions. The signal (information) is compared in the hippocampus with the long-term memory and then transfered back to the prefrontal cortex. The "created thought" induces over specific cell modules, in combination with specific electric excitations, the release of transmitters out of their vesicles, which then promotes via the nucleus an increased production of the neurotransmitter enzymes. The increased synthesis of the transmitter is then reported to the proper genetic apparatus, which results in a gene activation with augmented RNA-synthesis and respective m-RNA. The affected neurons show an increase in the number of ribosomes and, therefore, an augmentation of the respective intended protein synthesis will occur. The result is an increased amount of transmitter molecules and a change in the neurochemical constellation. This influences, depending on the location

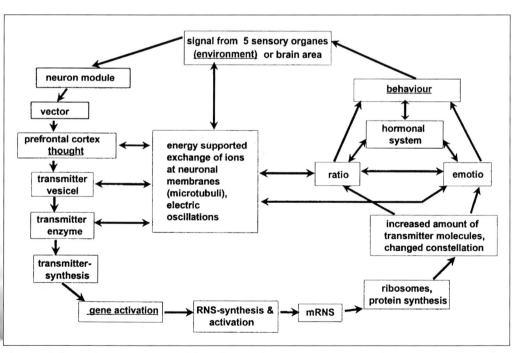

Fig. 11: Schematic presentation of the relations between the origin of thoughts, plasticity of the brain due to gene activation, behaviour and environment (HOLLMANN, 1998).

and form, the ratio (reason) and/or emotio (feeling). Especially the latter information is transfered over the hippocampus and pituitary to the hormonal system and induces an acute, environment-related behavior, based on the hormonal response adapted to the overall constellation (outside and inside world). This neuro-physico-chemical product – the thought – moves to the sensory areas of the brain (including cerebral areas of hormone production) and among others back to the prefrontal cortex. The last piece has fallen into place.

According to CHURCHLAND (1995), the cognitive activity only occurs in our consciousness, if it is represented as a vector of sequences of vectors within a spacious recurrent system. CRICK and KOCH (1990) assume, at least for visual attention the existence of a coordinated activity of neurons at 40 Hz in the layers 5 and 6. These layers are actually connected with recurrent loops of several systems; among these the thalamus and other subcortical structures. A similar opinion has been put forward by DAMASIO (1997) as well as LLINÁS and RIBARY (1993). The immense abilities of neuronal networks with recurrent systems and the building of vector concentrations have been demonstrated several times during the last years. Figure 11 schematically shows our hypothesis. It is based on the sum of experimental findings from many research groups.

Summary

The self-conscious mind is based on an immense arsenal of structures and functions, which are spread over the whole brain and the peripheral nervous system. The five sensory organs as well as the cerebrum-immanent world of memory and thoughts constantly report to several brain areas, which themselves are made up of blocks of neurons (modules). These modules are not stiff constructions but consist out of a large amount of physico-chemical circuits, which are built as a response to the constant reception of information from the outside and inside world. The accompanying synapses are part of a network and respond with the production of a variety of qualitatively and quantitatively different neurotransmitters, which then have a feedback effect on molecular (symbole molecules) and genetic level. *The brain is not hardware like a computer,* but – due to its physics, chemical and architectural plasticity – constantly reshaped by the incoming software. The existing or the resulting mental state, respectively, influence the behavior and, therefore, also the world of molecular signals within the individua systems. Thoughts have a causal effect on the neuronal activity as well as on the neuronal structures.

The physico-chemical function of the circuits and their respective neurotransmitters stand in a close mutual relation with the *areas of hormone production* in the body. Through feedback of the sensory and intellectual environment brain structures are constantly modified. The effects reach from structural, biophysical and biochemical areas to the molecular-biological and genetic apparatus. The neuron changes analogous to the skeletal muscles, in which exercise-induced cellular adaptations due to a primary influence on genes and the resulting modification of gene expression have been shown. *The individual cell systems are highly specialized for physics responsibilities, which can only be executed by the specific group of cells.* Pictures are not "seen", but electromagnetic waves are transfered from the retina of the eye into electric signals, which are forwarded over the nervus opticus to the occiptial brain. This is the location where the processing of all physics information takes place under integration of a feedback from relevant experiences (memory), and a picture is formed, which itself triggers thoughts (ratio) and emotions (emotio). In this process, the whole human organism is involved due to the peripheral nervous system and the feedback mechanism with areas of hormone production.

All in all, the human mind is a subjective construction. Because every human has different "experiences" with each physics or chemical sensation, they consequently lead to a more or less individually modified "self-construct". We do not have enough words to be able to precisely express in detail the scale of our feelings and emotions. Each human being is "a unique human being".

We have gained – particularly during the last $1^1/_2$ decades – a huge amount of new knowledge on the functioning of the human brain and the mind as its expression. In the end they are only physico-chemical mechanisms, which leave the underlying question unanswered: How is it possible that electrical impulses as energy-supported exchanges of ions located at neuronal membranes (especially in microtubuli), in combination with transmitter responses triggered by them, can create thoughts and feelings? In its extent this problem is comparable to the questions concerning the origin of all laws of physics and chemistry, which are of relevance at the furthest galaxies just as on earth.

References

ACHER, R. (1981): Evolution of neuropeptides. In: *Trends in Neurosciences, 9,* 225.

ADER, R. (1991): *Psychoneuroimmunology.* San Diego: Academic Press Geology Series.

AKIL, H.; WATSON, S. J.; YOUNG, E.; LEWIS, M. E.; KHACHATURIAN, H.; WALKER, J. M. (1984): Endogenous opioids: biology function. In: *Annual Review of Neuroscience, 7,* 223.

AMMON, H. P. T. (1984): Neue Aspekte zum Mechanismus der zentralerregenden Wirkung von Coffein. In: *Deutsche Medizinische Wochenschrift, 109,* 1491.

ARENTZ, T.; DE MEIRLEIR, K.; HOLLMANN, W. (1986): Die Rolle der endogenen opioiden Peptide während Fahrradergometerarbeit. In: *Deutsche Zeitschrift für Sportmedizin, 37* (7), 210.

BARTFAI, T.; IVERFELDT, K.; BRODIN, E.; OGREN, S. O. (1986): Functional consequences of coexistance of classical and peptide neurotransmitters. In: HÖKFELT, T.; FUXE, K.; PERNOW, B. (eds.): *Progress in brain research.* New York: Elsevier Science Publishers.

BIGUET, N. F.; BUDA, M.; LAMOUROUX, A.; SAMOLYK, D.; MALLET, J. (1986): Time course of the changes of THmRna in rat brain and adrenal medula after a single injection of reserpine. In: *EMBO Journal, 5,* 287.

BLACK, I. B.; ADLER, J. E.; DREYFUS, C. F.; FRIEDMAN, W. F.; LAGAMMA, E. F.; ROACH, A. H. (1987): Biochemistry of information storage in the nervous system. In: *Science, 236,* 1263.

BLACK, I. B. (1993): *Information in the brain.* Cambridge, MA.: The MIT Press.

BROWNSTEIN, M. J.; MEZEY, E. (1986): Multiple chemical messengers in hypothalamic

magnocellular neurones. In: Hökfelt, T.;
Fuxe, K.; Pernow, B. (eds.): *Progress in
brain research. Vol. 68.* New York: Elsevier
Science Publishers.

Calvin, W. (1990): *The cerebral symphony:
Seashore reflections on the structue of
consciousness.* New York: Bantam.

Cardelly-Cangiano, P.; Cangiano, C.; James,
H. J.; Ceci, F.; Fischer, J. E.; Strom, R.
(1984): Effect of ammonia on amino acid
uptake by brain microvessels. In: *Journal
of Biological Chemistry, 259,* 5295.

Changeux, J. P. (1984): *Der neuronale
Mensch.* Reinbek/Hamburg: Rowohlt.

Chaouloff, F. (1989): Physical exercise and
brain monoamines: a review. In: *Acta
Physiologica Scandinavica, 137,* 1.

Chaouloff, F. (1993): Physiopharmacological
interactions between stress hormones
and central serotonergic systems. In:
Brain Research Reviews, 18, 1.

Churchland, P. M. (1995): *The engine of
reason, the seat of the soul.* Massachusetts Institutes of Technology, Cambridge.

Cowan, W. M.; Fawcett, J. W.; O'Leary, D. D.
M.; Standfield, B. B. (1984): Regressive
events in neurogenesis. In: *Science, 225,*
1258.

Crick, F. H. C. (1994): *The estonishing hypothesis: The scientific search for the soul.*
New York: Charles Scribner's Sons.

Crick, F. H.; Koch, C. (1990): Towards a
neurobiological theory of consciousness.
In: Seminars in Neurosciences, 2, 263–275.

Damasio, A. R. (1997): *Descartes' Irrtum.*
München: Deutscher Taschenbuchverlag.

De Meirleir, K.; Arentz, T.; Hollmann, W.;
van Haelst, L. (1985a): The role of endogenous opiates in thermal regulation of
the body during exercise. In: *British
Medical Journal, 290,* 739.

De Meirleir, K.; Baeyens, L.; L'Hermite, M.;
L'Hermite-Balériaux, M.; Hollmann, W.
(1985b): Exercise-induced prolactin
release is related to anaerobiosis. In:
*Journal of Clinical Endocrinology and
Metabolism, 69,* 1250.

De Meirleir, K.; L'Hermite-Balériaux, M.;
L'Hermite, M.; Rost, R.; Hollmann, W.

(1985c): Evidence for serotoninergic
control of exercise-induced prolactin
secretion. In: *Hormone and Metabolic
Research, 17* (7), 380.

De Meirleir, K.; Smitz, J.; van Steirteghem,
A.; L'Hermite, M.; Hollmann, W. (1985d):
Dopaminergic and serotoninergic neurotransmitter systems involved in exercise-
induced release of adenohypophyseal
hormones. *6th Internat. Symposion
Biochem. of Exercise,* Copenhagen.

De Meirleir, K.; Gerlo, F.; Hollmann, W.;
van Haelst, L. (1987a): Cardiovascular
effects of pergolide mesylate during
dynamic exercise. In: *British Journal of
Clinical Pharmacology, 23* (5), 633.

De Meirleir, K.; Smitz, J.; van Steiteghem,
A.; Hollmann, W. (1987b): Serotonin anta-
gonism during exercise in man. In: *Acta
Cardiologica, XLII* (5), 360.

Du Bois-Reymond, E. (1872): *Über die
Grenzen des Naturerkennens.* Festvortrag
Humboldt-Universität, Berlin.

Du Bois-Reymond, E. (1874): *Festansprache
Humboldt-Universität,* Berlin.

Eccles, J. C. (1993): *Die Evolution des
Gehirns – Die Erschaffung des Selbst.*
München: Piper.

Eichenbaum, H.; Weiner, S. I.; Shapiro, M.;
Cohen, N. J. (1989): The organization of
spatial coding in the hippocampus: a
study of neural ensemble activity. In:
Journal of Neuroscience, 9, 2764.

Fischer, H. G.; Hollmann, W.; De Meirleir,
K. (1991): Exercise changes in plasma tryptophan fractions and relationship with
prolactin. In: *International Journal of
Sports Medicine, 12* (5), 487.

Gazzaniga, M. S. (1989): Organization of the
human brain. In: *Science, 245,* 947.

Gazzaniga, M. S.; LeDoux, J. E. (1978): *The
integrated mind.* New York: Plenum.

Goldman-Rakic, P. S. (1984): Modular organization of prefrontal cortex. In: *T I N S
Neurotoxins Supplement, 7,* 419.

Greenough, W. T. (1984): Structural correlates of information storage in the
mammalian brain: a review and hypothesis.
In: *T I N S Neurotoxins Supplement, 7,* 229.

HANLEY, M. R. (1989): Peptide regulatory factors in the nervous system. In: *Lancet, 1,* 1373.

HAWKING, St. D. (1988): *Eine kurze Geschichte der Zeit.* Reinbek/Hamburg: Rowohlt.

HERHOLZ, K.; BUSKIES, W.; RIST, M.; PAWLIK, G.; HOLLMANN, W.; HEISS, W. D. (1987): Regional cerebral blood flow in man at rest and during exercise. In: *Journal of neurology, 234,* 9.

HERZOG, H.; UNGER, V.; KUWERT, T. et al. (1992): Physical exercise does not increase cerebral metabolic rate of glucose utilization. XVIth Internat. Symposion on Cerebral Blood Flow and Metabolism. Miami, USA.

HOLLMANN, W. (1963): Höchst- und Dauerleistungsfähigkeit des Sportlers. München: Barth.

HOLLMANN, W.; FISCHER, H. G.; DE MEIRLEIR, K.; HERHOLZ, K.; FEINENDEGEN, L. E. (1994): The brain – regional cerebral blood flow, metabolism, and psyche during ergometer exercise. In: Bouchard, C.; Shephard, R. J.; Stephens, T. (eds.): *Physical activity, fitness, and health (International Proceedings and Consensus Statement), World-Consensus-Congress in Toronto.* Champaign, IL.: Human Kinetics.

HOLLMANN, W.; DE MEIRLEIR, K.; FISCHER, H. G.; HOLZGRAEFE, M. (1993): Über neuere Aspekte von Gehirn, Muskelarbeit, Sport und Psyche. In: *Deutsche Zeitschrift für Sportmedizin, 44* (10), 478.

HOLLMANN, W.; STRÜDER, H. K. (1998): Das menschliche Gehirn als Agitator und Rezeptor von muskulärer Arbeit. Dtsch. Z. Sportmed. 49 (Sonderheft 1) 154–160.

HOLLMANN, W.; STRÜDER, H. K.; HERZOG, H.; FISCHER, H. G.; PLATEN, P.; DE MEIRLEIR, K. L.; DONIKE, M. (1996): Gehirn – hämodynamische, metabolische und psychische Aspekte bei körperlicher Arbeit. In: *Deutsches Ärzteblatt, 93,* 2033.

HUGHES, J.; SMITH, T. W.; KOSTERLITZ, H. W.; FOTHERGILL, L. A.; MORGAN, M. A.; MORRIS, H. R. (1975): Identification of two related pentapeptides from the brain with potent opiate agonist activity. In: Nature, 258, 577.

KESSLER, J. A.; ADLER, J. E.; BLACK, I. B. (1983): Substance P and somatostatin regulate sympathetic noradrenergic function. In: *Science, 221,* 1059.

KORNHUBER, H. H. (1973): Neural control of input into long-term memory. Limbic system and amnestic syndrome in man. In: ZIPPEL, H. P. (ed.): *Memory and transfer of information.* New York: Plenum Press.

LASSEN, N. A.; INGVAR, D. H.; SKINHÖJ, E. (1985): *Hirnfunktion und Hirndurchblutung.* Heidelberg: Spektrum der Wissenschaft.

LATASTE, X. (1992): The blood-brain-barrier in hypoxia. In: *International Journal of Sports Medicine, 13,* 45.

LIBET, B. (1981): Timing of cerebral processes relative to concomittant conscious experiences in man. In: ADAM, G.; MESZAROS, I.; BANJAI, E. I. (eds.): *Advances in physiological science.* Elmsford/New York: Pergamon.

LIBET, B. (1982): Brain stimulation in the study of neuronal functions for conscious sensory experiences. In: *Human Neurobiology, 1,* 235.

LIBET, B. (1985): Unconscious cerebral initiative and the role of conscious will in voluntary action. In: *Behavioral and Brain Sciences, 8,* 529.

LIBET, B. (1993): The neural time factor in conscious and unconscious events. In: CIBA Foundation Symposion 174 (eds.): *Experimental and theoretical studies of consciousness.* Chichester, UK: Wiley.

LIBET, B.; GLEASON, C. A.; WRIGHT, W. E.; PEARL, D. K. (1983): Time of conscious intention to act in relation to onset of cerebral activities (readyness-potential); the unconscious initiation of a freely voluntary act. In: *Brain, 106,* 623.

LLINÁS, R.; RIBARY, U. (1993): Coherent 40-Hz oszillation characterizes dream state in humans. In: *Proceedings of the National Academy of Science of the United States of America, 90,* 2078.

LYNCH, G. (1986): *Synapses, circuits, and the beginnings of memory.* Cambridge, MA: MIT Press.

MANS, A. M.; BIEBUYCK, J. F.; HAWKINS, R. A. (1983): Ammonia selectively stimulates neutral amino acid transport across blood-brain barrier. In: *American Journal of Physiology, 245*, 74.

MANS, A. M.; BIEBUYCK, J. F.; HAWKINS, R. A. (1987): Brain tryptophan abnormalities in hyperammoneamia and liver disease. In: BENDER, D. A.; JOSEPH, M. H.; KOCHEN, W.; STEINHALT, H. (eds.): *Progress in tryptophan and serotonin research 1986*. Berlin: De Gruyter.

MELANDER, S. (1960): Comparative studies on the adrenergic neurohormonal control of resistance and carpacitance blood vessels in the cat. In: *Acta Physiologica Scandinavica Supplementum, 50*, 176.

MÜLLER, R. A.; THOENEN, H.; AXELROD, J. (1969): Increase in tyrosine hydroxylase activity after reserpine administration. In: *Journal of Pharmacology and Experimental Therapeutics, 169*, 74.

NAUTA, W.; FEIRTAG, M. (1990): *Neuroanatomie*. Heidelberg: Spektrum der Wissenschaft.

NICOLL, R. A. (1988): The coupling of neurotransmitter receptors to ion channels in the brain. In: *Science, 241*, 545.

NITSCH, J. R. (1981): *Stress-Theorien, Untersuchungen, Maßnahmen*. Bern/Stuttgart/Wien: Huber.

NITSCH, J. R. (1976): Die Eigenzustandsskala (EZ-Skala) – Ein Verfahren zur hierarchisch-mehrdimensionalen Befindlichkeitsskalierung. In: NITSCH, J. R.; UDRIS, I. (eds.): *Beanspruchung im Sport*. Bad Homburg: Limpert, 81-102.

PENROSE, R. (1991): *Computerdenken*. Heidelberg: Spektrum der Wissenschaft.

PLATEN, P.; GOTZMANN, A.; KEIZER, H.; DONIKE, M.; EVERTZ, S.; GOLTERMANN, S.; SANDER, U. (1993): Differences in the exercise-induced changes of serum tryptophan (TRP) and the large neutral amino acid (LNAA)/TRP-ratio in anorectic and the eumenorrheic runners. In: *Medicine and Science in Sports and Exercise, 25*, (5), 431.

PÖPPEL, E. (1996): Grenzen des Bewußtseins. In: METZINGER, T. (ed.): *Bewußtsein*. Paderborn/München: Schöningh.

ROLAND, P. E.; LARSEN, B. (1976): Focal increase of cerebral blood flow during stereognostic testing in man. In: *Archives of Neurology, 33*, 551.

ROLAND, P. E.; LARSEN, B.; LASSEN, N. A.; SKINHÖJ, E. (1980): Supplementary motor area and other cortical areas in organization of voluntary movements in man. In: *Journal of Neurophysiology, 43*, 118.

ROTH, E. (1994): *Das Gehirn und seine Wirklichkeit*. Frankfurt/M: Suhrkamp.

SCHLICHT, H. J. (1995): Anwendung und professionelle Nutzung der Kodak Photo CD. Bonn: Addison-Wesley.

SINGER, W.; ARTOLA, A.; ENGEL, A. K.; KÖNIG, P.; KREITER, A. K.; LOWEL, S.; SCHILLEN, T. B. (1993): Neuronal representations and temporal codes. In: POGGIO, T. A.; GLASER, D. A. (eds.): *Exploring brain functions: models in neuroscience*. Chichester/New York: John Wiley & Sons.

SNYDER, D. M. (1988): On the time of a conscious peripheral sensation. In: *Journal of Theoretical Biology, 130*, 253.

SPERRY, R. W. (1981): Cerebral organization and behavior. In: *Science, 133*, 1749.

SPITZER, M. (1998): History of neural networks. In: STEIN, D. (ed.): *Neural networks and psychopathology*. Cambridge: Cambridge University Press.

STRÜDER, H. K.; HOLLMANN, W.; PLATEN, P.; WÖSTMANN, R.; WEICKER, H.; MOLDERINGS, G. H. (1999a): Effect of acute and chronic exercise on plasma amino acids and prolactin concentrations and on [^{3}H]ketanserin binding to 5-HT$_{2A}$ receptors on human platelets. In: *European Journal of Applied Physiology and Occupational Physiology, 79*, 318.

STRÜDER, H. K.; HOLLMANN, W.; WEICKER, H.; SCHIFFER, T.; WEBER, K. (1999b): Blood oxygen pressure affects plasma prolactin concentration in humans. In: *Acta Physiologica Scandinavica Supplementum, 165*, 265.

STRÜDER, H. K.; HOLLMANN, W.; PLATEN, P.;

Brain, Psyche, Mind, and Muscular Activity

DONIKE, M.; GOTZMANN, A.; WEBER, K. (1998a): Influence of paroxetine, branched-chain amino acids and tyrosine on neuroendocrine system responses and fatigue in humans. In: *Hormone and Metabolic Research, 30,* 188.

STRÜDER, H. K.; HOLLMANN, W.; PLATEN, P.; ROST, R.; WEICKER, H.; KIRCHHOF, O.; WEBER, K. (1999c): Neuroendocrine system and mental function in sedentary and endurance-trained elderly males. In: *International Journal of Sports Medicine, 20,* 159.

STRÜDER, H. K.; HOLLMANN, W.; PLATEN, P.; ROST, R.; WEICKER, H.; WEBER, K. (1998b): Hypothalamic-pituitary-adrenal and – gonadal axis function after exercise in sedentary and endurance trained elderly males. In: *European Journal of Applied Physiology and Occupational Physiology, 77,* 285.

STRÜDER, H. K.; HOLLMANN, W.; PLATEN, P.; WÖSTMANN, R.; FERRAUTI, A.; WEBER, K. (1997): Effects of exercise intensity on free tryptophan to branched-chain amino acids ratio and plasma prolactin during endurance exercise. In: *Canadian Journal of Applied Physiology, 22,* 280.

STRÜDER, H. K.; HOLLMANN, W.; DONIKE, M.; PLATEN, P.; WEBER, K. (1996a): Effect of O_2 availability on neuroendocrine variables at rest and during execise: O_2-breathing increases plasma prolactin. In: *European Journal of Applied Physiology and Occupational Physiology, 74,* 443.

STRÜDER, H. K.; HOLLMANN, W.; PLATEN, P. (1996b): Increased prolactin response to hyperoxia at rest and during exercise. In: *International Journal of Sports Medicine, 17,* 390.

STRÜDER, H. K.; HOLLMANN, W.; PLATEN, P.; DUPERLY, J.; FISCHER, H. G.; WEBER, K. (1996c): Alterations in plasma free tryptophan and large neutral amino acids do not affect perceived exertion and prolactin during 90 min of treadmill exercise. In: *International Journal of Sports Medicine, 17,* 73.

SUTTER, A.; HOSANG, M.; VALE, R. D.; SHOOTER, E. M. (1984): The interaction of nerve growth factor with its specific receptors. In: BLACK, I. B. (ed.): *Cellular and molecular biology of neuronal development.* New York: Plenum Press.

THOENEN, H.; MÜLLER, R. A.; AXELROD, J. (1970): Phase difference in the induction of tyrosine hydroxylase in cell body and nerve terminals of sympathetic neurons. In: *Proceedings of the National Academy of Science of the United States of America, 65,* 58.

UHLENBRUCK, G.; ORDER, U. (1987): Perspektiven, Probleme und Prioritäten: Sportimmunologie – die nächsten 75 Jahre? In: *Deutsche Zeitschrift für Sportmedizin, (Sondernummer)* 4.

WILSON, M. A.; MCNAUGHTON, B. L. (1993): Dynamics of the hippocampal ensemble code for space. In: *Science, 261,* 1055.

WU, K.; BLACK, I. B. (1989): Regulation of synaptic molecular architecture in a rat sympathetic ganglion and hippocampus. In: *Journal of Cognitive Neuroscience, 1,* 194.

ZIGMOND, R. E.; SCHWARZSCHILD, M. A.; RITTENHOUSE, A. R. (1989): Acute regulation of tyrosine hydroxylase by nerve activity and by neurotransmitters via phosphorylation. In: *Annual Review of Neuroscience, 12,* 415.

Authors Biographies

Age-Specific Physical Activities and Other Lifeway Patterns
Influencing Health and Longevity

Ralph S. Paffenbarger, Jr.

Ralph S. Paffenbarger, Jr., MD, Dr. Ph., Sc.D h.c., Professor
of Epidemiology, Emeritus (Active) at Stanford University
School of Medicine was born in Columbus, Ohio on 21
October 1922. He was educated at Ohio State University,
Columbus, at the Northwestern University Medical School,
Chicago and at the John Hopkins University, School of
Hygiene and Public Health, Baltimore. In 1977 he became
Professor of Epidemiology at Stanford University School of
Medicine. Interested in preventive medicine and public
health, Dr. Paffenbarger's earlier research focussed on
infectious disease epidemiology with special attention to
the identification of the mechanisms of transmission and
the pathogenesis of poliomyelitis. In the mid 1950's he
focussed his research on chronic disease epidemiology and the search for causes of 1)
mental illnesses associated with childbearing, 2) site-specific cancers, and 3) cardio-
vascular-hypertensive-metabolic diseases. Beginning in the late 1950's, Dr. Paffenbarger's research concentrated on physical activity as it relates to the development of
cardiovascular and other chronic diseases (diabetes mellitus, obesity, selected
cancers, and neurological diseases) among college alumni, San Francisco Bay Area
longshoremen, and other populations. In 1960 he founded the College Alumni Health
Study, which has chronicled the physical activity levels, other lifeway habits, and
personal characteristics of 71.044 alumni and alumnae from Harvard College and the
University of Pennsylvania. These habit patterns and characteristics have been
studied for their relation of the development and progression of chronic diseases and
to their effect on longevity. Some of his honors are the Joseph B. Wolffe Lecture and
Award, American College of Sports Medicine (1988), the American College of Sports
Medicine Honor Award (1994), the First IOC Olympic Prize for Sports Sciences which is
shared with Prof. Jeremy N. Morris (July 14, 1996), and the IOC Olympic Academy of
Sports Sciences (1999).

Genetic Aspects of Physical Activity, Cardiorespiratory Fitness
and the Response to Regular Exercise

Tuomo Rankinen

Tuomo Rankinen studied Clinical Nutrition at the University of Kuopio, Finland. He graduated in 1996 from the same University as a Ph.D. In 1999 he completed post-doctoral studies at Physical Activity Sciences Laboratory, Laval University. At present he is instructor and Project Director of the Heritage Family Study at the Pennington Biomedical Research Center and Human Genomics Laboratory in Louisiana. At the International 13th and 14th Puijo Symposium he performed as Scientific Secretary. Furthermore in 1993 he was honoured with the Martti J. Karvonen Award. Tuomo Rankinen is a member of several associations like the International Ateriosclerosis Society, the Finish Society for Nutrition Research, the American College of Sports Medicine and several other associations and more.

Louis Pérusse

Dr. Louis Pérusse is an adjunct professor in the Division of Kinesiology in the department of preventive medicine at Laval University in Quebec. He graduated in physical activity sciences from University Laval as a M.Sc. and Ph.D. He has also completed post-doctoral studies in human genetics at the University of Michigan at Ann Arbor.
Dr. Pérusse's research focuses on the genetic and molecular epidemiology of obesity and its co-morbidities as well as of various determinants of physical fitness and performance, cardiovascular disease risk factors and their adaptation to exercise training. He is a member of the American College of Sports Medicine and the American Society of Human Genetics. Dr. Pérusse is co-author of the book Genetics of Fitness and Physical Performance and published more than 150 professional and scientific papers.

Claude Bouchard

Claude Bouchard, Ph.D., Professor and Executive Director, George A. Bray Chair in Nutrition at the Louisiana State University, Pennington Biomedical Research Center. He was educated at the Laval University and the University of Oregon in Exercise Physiology. In 1977 he graduated in Population Genetics from the University of Texas, Austin as a Ph.D. From 1997 until 1999 he had the chair of Kinesiology at the Laval University, Department of Social and Preventive Medicine, Faculty of Medicine. At present he is president elect of the International Association for the Study of Obesity and member of several associations like the Scientific Advisory Committee of Weight Watchers International, the Science Board of the Institutes Of Pharmaceutical Discovery, the Board of the Cooper Aerobics Research Institute and more. He is also author or co-author of more than 600 research papers and 600 oral presentations.

Ppysical Activity and the Immune System – for the Better and the Worse

Bente Klarlund Pedersen

Bente Klarlund Pedersen: MD, Dr. Med. Sc., graduated from the Copenhagen University in 1983 as a medical doctor. She is a specialist in internal medicine and infectious medicine, and works as a clinician and researcher in the Department of Infectious Diseases at Rigshospitalet in Copenhagen, Denmark. Dr. Pedersen`s research focus has been exercise and stress immunology, HIV immunology and aging immunology with more than 230 peer-reviewed publications. She is the author of Exercise Immunology, published in 1997 by Springer and Co-author of Nutrition and Exercise Immunology published in 2000 by CRC Press. Dr. Pedersen is an associate editor of the journal of The Danish Medical association and member of the editorial board of the European Journal of Applied Physiology. She is president of The Danish Society of Infectious Diseases and past-president of the International Society of Exercise and Immunology.

Wildor Hollmann

Univ. Prof. mult. Dr. med. Dr. h.c. Wildor Hollmann was born in Menden/Sauerland on 30 January 1925. He began his scientific career with his dissertation at the Medical University Clinic Cologne and the German Sport University Cologne in 1949. In 1954 he introduced the bike spiroergometry to the Medical University Clinic Cologne from where it was disseminated worldwide. In collaboration with Sander he developed the blood pressure measurement during physical activity in 1955 and in 1959 the principle of the aerob-anaerob threshold by determination of ventilation and lactate acid. In 1961 he habilitated at the University of Cologne in the field of "sports medicine" and was offered and accepted the position as chair for cardiology and sports medicine at the German Sport University Cologne on 1 January 1965. In 1958 Prof. Hollmann founded the Institute of Cardiology and Sports Medicine as a "one-man enterprise" in Cologne. Subsequently it produced numerous habilitations and nominations of chairs. For 14 years Prof. Hollmann was rector of the German Sport University Cologne. Further posts included prorector and dean of the German Sport University Cologne, president of the World Council of Sports Medicine for eight years and president of the German Federation of Sport Doctors and president of the German Olympic Society for three years. He was honoured with a number of international and national awards in the areas of medicine, cardiology and gerontology. The focal points of research concerned the influence of work, training and physical activity on heart, circulation, ventilation, metabolism, hormonal regulation as well as since 1985 on blood flow, circulation and metabolism behaviour of the brain and on the psyche.

Heiko K. Strüder

PD Dr. Heiko K. Strüder: born 1965; 1984-1989 studies of Exercise Science and English at the German Sport University Cologne, the University of Cologne and the Northwest Missouri State University (USA); 1993 Ph.D. in Exercise Science at the Insitute for Cardiology and Sports Medicine of the German Sport University Cologne; 1999 Habilitation for Exercise Physiology and Endocrinology at the same university with the thesis titled "Influence of muscular work on brain metabolism and psyche in trained and untrained males of different ages. The monoaminergic and neuroendocrine system"; since 2000 working at the Institute for Theory and Practice of  Training and Movement of the German Sport University Cologne; Managing Editor of the European Journal of Sports Science; working in performance diagnosis in top performance and recreational sports; main research area is focussed on the effects of exercise and training on the brain; received several awards for research such as in 1993 the "Arno Arnold Award" of the German Association of Sports Medicine and Prevention.

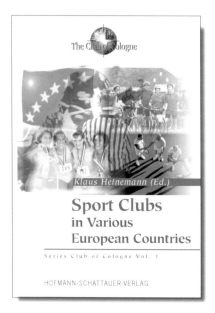

Klaus Heinemann (Ed.)

Sport Clubs in Various European Countries

Series Club of Cologne Vol. 1

1999. Size 16,5 × 24 cm, 372 Pages
ISBN 3-7780-6001-5
(Order-Number 6001)
€ 19,80

This book deals with the situation of sports and sports clubs in 11 European countries: Finland, Norway, Denmark, Great Britain, Belgium, Germany, Poland, Switzerland, France, Italy and Spain. Renowned scientists of each of these countries were acquired as authors. This volume ends with a comparison of sports organisations in Europe and North America by a Canadian scientist.

The individual articles go beyond mere description. In addition to the portrayal of the peculiarities and the diversity of sports organisations and the specific problems the clubs in the different countries are confronted with, substantial information regarding the historical development, the characteristics of its integration in society, the relationship of sports and politics and the versatile functions of sports and its clubs are thematised.

Thus it becomes obvious that sports and its organisations are part of the culture and the tradition of a respective country which makes them indispensable for its individual identity, its sense of belonging together and its possibility of social integration.

This volume fulfils important expectations and tasks the Club of Cologne is devoted to. It intends to describe developments in the area of sports and to point out possible dangers and hazards, which could eventually arise. This publication can raise attention to the fact that it must be one task of politics to protect the characteristics of sports and its organisations as part of the respective national culture since they fulfil important social functions.

 **Verlag Karl Hofmann** Postfach 1360, 73603 Schorndorf
Tel. (0 71 81) 402-125, Fax (0 71 81) 402-111 E-Mail: hofmann@hofmann-verlag.de